The Closing Academy

THE ULTIMATE SALES PLANNER FOR THE MASTER CLOSER

Plan And Schedule Your Activities
To Achieve Your Sales Goals

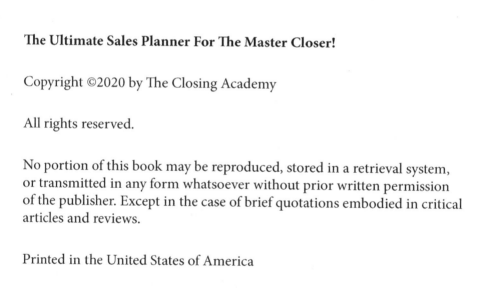

The Ultimate Sales Planner For The Master Closer!

Copyright ©2020 by The Closing Academy

Printed in the United States of America

Published by The Closing Academy
Loganville, GA
theclosingacademy.com

ISBN 978-1-7337833-1-6

This Planner
Belongs to:

Your Name: _____

Phone: _____

Email: _____

Your Sales Journey Starts Here!

Today's Date: _____

Plan Your Day, Take Action and Achieve Your Sales Goals!

2021

JANUARY

S	M	T	W	T	F	S
					1	2
3	4	5	6	7	8	9
10	11	12	13	14	15	16
17	18	19	20	21	22	23
24 31	25	26	27	28	29	30

FEBRUARY

S	M	T	W	T	F	S
	1	2	3	4	5	6
7	8	9	10	11	12	13
14	15	16	17	18	19	20
21	22	23	24	25	26	27
28						

MARCH

S	M	T	W	T	F	S
	1	2	3	4	5	6
7	8	9	10	11	12	13
14	15	16	17	18	19	20
21	22	23	24	25	26	27
28	29	30	31			

APRIL

S	M	T	W	T	F	S
				1	2	3
4	5	6	7	8	9	10
11	12	13	14	15	16	17
18	19	20	21	22	23	24
25	26	27	28	29	30	

MAY

S	M	T	W	T	F	S
						1
2	3	4	5	6	7	8
9	10	11	12	13	14	15
16	17	18	19	20	21	22
23 30	24 31	25	26	27	28	29

JUNE

S	M	T	W	T	F	S
		1	2	3	4	5
6	7	8	9	10	11	12
13	14	15	16	17	18	19
20	21	22	23	24	25	26
27	28	29	30			

JULY

S	M	T	W	T	F	S
				1	2	3
4	5	6	7	8	9	10
11	12	13	14	15	16	17
18	19	20	21	22	23	24
25	26	27	28	29	30	31

AUGUST

S	M	T	W	T	F	S
1	2	3	4	5	6	7
8	9	10	11	12	13	14
15	16	17	18	19	20	21
22	23	24	25	26	27	28
29	30	31				

SEPTEMBER

S	M	T	W	T	F	S
			1	2	3	4
5	6	7	8	9	10	11
12	13	14	15	16	17	18
19	20	21	22	23	24	25
26	27	28	29	30		

OCTOBER

S	M	T	W	T	F	S
					1	2
3	4	5	6	7	8	9
10	11	12	13	14	15	16
17	18	19	20	21	22	23
24 31	25	26	27	28	29	30

NOVEMBER

S	M	T	W	T	F	S
	1	2	3	4	5	6
7	8	9	10	11	12	13
14	15	16	17	18	19	20
21	22	23	24	25	26	27
28	29	30				

DECEMBER

S	M	T	W	T	F	S
			1	2	3	4
5	6	7	8	9	10	11
12	13	14	15	16	17	18
19	20	21	22	23	24	25
26	27	28	29	30	31	

2022

JANUARY

S	M	T	W	T	F	S
						1
2	3	4	5	6	7	8
9	10	11	12	13	14	15
16	17	18	19	20	21	22
23 30	24 31	25	26	27	28	29

FEBRUARY

S	M	T	W	T	F	S
		1	2	3	4	5
6	7	8	9	10	11	12
13	14	15	16	17	18	19
20	21	22	23	24	25	26
27	28					

MARCH

S	M	T	W	T	F	S
		1	2	3	4	5
6	7	8	9	10	11	12
13	14	15	16	17	18	19
20	21	22	23	24	25	26
27	28	29	30	31		

APRIL

S	M	T	W	T	F	S
					1	2
3	4	5	6	7	8	9
10	11	12	13	14	15	16
17	18	19	20	21	22	23
24	25	26	27	28	29	30

MAY

S	M	T	W	T	F	S
1	2	3	4	5	6	7
8	9	10	11	12	13	14
15	16	17	18	19	20	21
22	23	24	25	26	27	28
29	30	31				

JUNE

S	M	T	W	T	F	S
			1	2	3	4
5	6	7	8	9	10	11
12	13	14	15	16	17	18
19	20	21	22	23	24	25
26	27	28	29	30		

JULY

S	M	T	W	T	F	S
					1	2
3	4	5	6	7	8	9
10	11	12	13	14	15	16
17	18	19	20	21	22	23
24 31	25	26	27	28	29	30

AUGUST

S	M	T	W	T	F	S
	1	2	3	4	5	6
7	8	9	10	11	12	13
14	15	16	17	18	19	20
21	22	23	24	25	26	27
28	29	30	31			

SEPTEMBER

S	M	T	W	T	F	S
				1	2	3
4	5	6	7	8	9	10
11	12	13	14	15	16	17
18	19	20	21	22	23	24
25	26	27	28	29	30	

OCTOBER

S	M	T	W	T	F	S
						1
2	3	4	5	6	7	8
9	10	11	12	13	14	15
16	17	18	19	20	21	22
23 30	24 31	25	26	27	28	29

NOVEMBER

S	M	T	W	T	F	S
		1	2	3	4	5
6	7	8	9	10	11	12
13	14	15	16	17	18	19
20	21	22	23	24	25	26
27	28	29	30			

DECEMBER

S	M	T	W	T	F	S
				1	2	3
4	5	6	7	8	9	10
11	12	13	14	15	16	17
18	19	20	21	22	23	24
25	26	27	28	29	30	31

2023

JANUARY

S	M	T	W	T	F	S
1	2	3	4	5	6	7
8	9	10	11	12	13	14
15	16	17	18	19	20	21
22	23	24	25	26	27	28
29	30	31				

FEBRUARY

S	M	T	W	T	F	S
			1	2	3	4
5	6	7	8	9	10	11
12	13	14	15	16	17	18
19	20	21	22	23	24	25
26	27	28				

MARCH

S	M	T	W	T	F	S
			1	2	3	4
5	6	7	8	9	10	11
12	13	14	15	16	17	18
19	20	21	22	23	24	25
26	27	28	29	30	31	

APRIL

S	M	T	W	T	F	S
						1
2	3	4	5	6	7	8
9	10	11	12	13	14	15
16	17	18	19	20	21	22
23 30	24	25	26	27	28	29

MAY

S	M	T	W	T	F	S
	1	2	3	4	5	6
7	8	9	10	11	12	13
14	15	16	17	18	19	20
21	22	23	24	25	26	27
28	29	30	31			

JUNE

S	M	T	W	T	F	S
				1	2	3
4	5	6	7	8	9	10
11	12	13	14	15	16	17
18	19	20	21	22	23	24
25	26	27	28	29	30	

JULY

S	M	T	W	T	F	S
						1
2	3	4	5	6	7	8
9	10	11	12	13	14	15
16	17	18	19	20	21	22
23 30	24 31	25	26	27	28	29

AUGUST

S	M	T	W	T	F	S
		1	2	3	4	5
6	7	8	9	10	11	12
13	14	15	16	17	18	19
20	21	22	23	24	25	26
27	28	29	30	31		

SEPTEMBER

S	M	T	W	T	F	S
					1	2
3	4	5	6	7	8	9
10	11	12	13	14	15	16
17	18	19	20	21	22	23
24	25	26	27	28	29	30

OCTOBER

S	M	T	W	T	F	S
1	2	3	4	5	6	7
8	9	10	11	12	13	14
15	16	17	18	19	20	21
22	23	24	25	26	27	28
29	30	31				

NOVEMBER

S	M	T	W	T	F	S
			1	2	3	4
5	6	7	8	9	10	11
12	13	14	15	16	17	18
19	20	21	22	23	24	25
26	27	28	29	30		

DECEMBER

S	M	T	W	T	F	S
					1	2
3	4	5	6	7	8	9
10	11	12	13	14	15	16
17	18	19	20	21	22	23
24 31	25	26	27	28	29	30

2024

JANUARY

S	M	T	W	T	F	S
	1	2	3	4	5	6
7	8	9	10	11	12	13
14	15	16	17	18	19	20
21	22	23	24	25	26	27
28	29	30	31			

FEBRUARY

S	M	T	W	T	F	S
				1	2	3
4	5	6	7	8	9	10
11	12	13	14	15	16	17
18	19	20	21	22	23	24
25	26	27	28	29		

MARCH

S	M	T	W	T	F	S
					1	2
3	4	5	6	7	8	9
10	11	12	13	14	15	16
17	18	19	20	21	22	23
24 31	25	26	27	28	29	30

APRIL

S	M	T	W	T	F	S
	1	2	3	4	5	6
7	8	9	10	11	12	13
14	15	16	17	18	19	20
21	22	23	24	25	26	27
28	29	30				

MAY

S	M	T	W	T	F	S
			1	2	3	4
5	6	7	8	9	10	11
12	13	14	15	16	17	18
19	20	21	22	23	24	25
26	27	28	29	30	31	

JUNE

S	M	T	W	T	F	S
						1
2	3	4	5	6	7	8
9	10	11	12	13	14	15
16	17	18	19	20	21	22
23 30	24	25	26	27	28	29

JULY

S	M	T	W	T	F	S
	1	2	3	4	5	6
7	8	9	10	11	12	13
14	15	16	17	18	19	20
21	22	23	24	25	26	27
28	29	30	31			

AUGUST

S	M	T	W	T	F	S
				1	2	3
4	5	6	7	8	9	10
11	12	13	14	15	16	17
18	19	20	21	22	23	24
25	26	27	28	29	30	31

SEPTEMBER

S	M	T	W	T	F	S
1	2	3	4	5	6	7
8	9	10	11	12	13	14
15	16	17	18	19	20	21
22	23	24	25	26	27	28
29	30					

OCTOBER

S	M	T	W	T	F	S
		1	2	3	4	5
6	7	8	9	10	11	12
13	14	15	16	17	18	19
20	21	22	23	24	25	26
27	28	29	30	31		

NOVEMBER

S	M	T	W	T	F	S
					1	2
3	4	5	6	7	8	9
10	11	12	13	14	15	16
17	18	19	20	21	22	23
24	25	26	27	28	29	30

DECEMBER

S	M	T	W	T	F	S
1	2	3	4	5	6	7
8	9	10	11	12	13	14
15	16	17	18	19	20	21
22	23	24	25	26	27	28
29	30	31				

How to Use
This Planner

Congratulations on taking your first step to mastering sales! This planner will guide you to this goal, but it will take work and dedication from you. Like any goal, you will need to invest your time. It is important that you sit down every day to map out where you are headed. You can review your progress weekly and monthly and make adjustments as needed. You must be committed to the process in order for you to accomplish your goals. This planner will be an excellent source for tracking your sales goals, monitoring your progress, and scheduling your day-to-day activities and appointments. Using this planner consistently will help you to become more organized and, when you become more organized, you will begin to clearly see your goals and, ultimately, achieve your sales goals!

The Master Plan

Vision Board

Vision Board

CREATE YOUR FUTURE

YEARLY GOALS

- [ ]
- [ ]
- [ ]
- [ ]
- [ ]
- [ ]

MOTIVATION

What is your WHY?

ACTION PLAN/ STRATEGY

- [ ]
- [ ]
- [ ]
- [ ]
- [ ]
- [ ]

NOTES

MONTH _____

SUNDAY	MONDAY	TUESDAY	WEDNESDAY

Sales is a teachable skill. – *Calbert Coakley*

THURSDAY	FRIDAY	SATURDAY	NOTES

DATE

M   T   W   Th   F   Sa   Su

To Do

- [ ]
- [ ]
- [ ]
- [ ]
- [ ]
- [ ]
- [ ]
- [ ]
- [ ]
- [ ]
- [ ]

Income Generating Activities

APPOINTMENTS

6am	
7am	
8am	
9am	
10am	
11am	
12pm	
1pm	
2pm	
3pm	
4pm	
5pm	
6pm	
7pm	

AFFIRMATIONS

SALES GOALS

NOTES / IDEAS

DATE			M	T	W	Th	F	Sa	Su

▷
▷
▷

To Do

- ☐
- ☐
- ☐
- ☐
- ☐
- ☐
- ☐
- ☐
- ☐
- ☐

Income Generating Activities

APPOINTMENTS

6am
7am
8am
9am
10am
11am
12pm
1pm
2pm
3pm
4pm
5pm
6pm
7pm

▷ AFFIRMATIONS

▷ SALES GOALS

▷ NOTES / IDEAS

DATE

M T W Th F Sa Su

TODAY'S TOP 3

▷ _____

▷ _____

▷ _____

To Do

- ☐ _____
- ☐ _____
- ☐ _____
- ☐ _____
- ☐ _____
- ☐ _____
- ☐ _____
- ☐ _____
- ☐ _____
- ☐ _____
- ☐ _____

Income Generating Activities

APPOINTMENTS

6am	▷ **AFFIRMATIONS**
7am	
8am	
9am	
10am	
11am	▷ **SALES GOALS**
12pm	
1pm	
2pm	
3pm	
4pm	▷ **NOTES / IDEAS**
5pm	
6pm	
7pm	

DATE

M   T   W   Th   F   Sa   Su

▷

▷

▷

TODAY'S TOP 3

To Do

- ☐
- ☐
- ☐
- ☐
- ☐
- ☐
- ☐
- ☐
- ☐
- ☐
- ☐

Income Generating Activities

APPOINTMENTS

6am

7am

8am

9am

10am

11am

12pm

1pm

2pm

3pm

4pm

5pm

6pm

7pm

▷ AFFIRMATIONS

▷ SALES GOALS

▷ NOTES / IDEAS

M   T   W   Th   F   Sa   Su

TODAY'S TOP 3

To Do

- ☐
- ☐
- ☐
- ☐
- ☐
- ☐
- ☐
- ☐
- ☐
- ☐
- ☐

Income Generating Activities

APPOINTMENTS

6am	
7am	
8am	
9am	
10am	
11am	
12pm	
1pm	
2pm	
3pm	
4pm	
5pm	
6pm	
7pm	

AFFIRMATIONS

SALES GOALS

NOTES / IDEAS

DATE

M   T   W   Th   F   Sa   Su

TODAY'S TOP 3

▷
▷
▷

To Do

☐
☐
☐
☐
☐
☐
☐
☐
☐
☐
☐

Income Generating Activities

APPOINTMENTS

6am
7am
8am
9am
10am
11am
12pm
1pm
2pm
3pm
4pm
5pm
6pm
7pm

▷ AFFIRMATIONS

▷ SALES GOALS

▷ NOTES / IDEAS

DATE

M   T   W   Th   F   Sa   Su

▷ _____

▷ _____

▷ _____

TODAY'S TOP 3

To Do

☐ _____

☐ _____

☐ _____

☐ _____

☐ _____

☐ _____

☐ _____

☐ _____

☐ _____

☐ _____

Income Generating Activities

APPOINTMENTS

6am

7am

8am

9am

10am

11am

12pm

1pm

2pm

3pm

4pm

5pm

6pm

7pm

▷ AFFIRMATIONS

▷ SALES GOALS

▷ NOTES / IDEAS

THIS WEEK IN REVIEW

This Week's Big Wins

☐ _____

☐ _____

☐ _____

☐ _____

☐ _____

☐ _____

☐ _____

☐ _____

NOTES

_____

_____

_____

_____

_____

NEXT WEEK AT A GLANCE

MON _____

TUE _____

WED _____

THU _____

FRI _____

SAT _____

SUN _____

DATE

M   T   W   Th   F   Sa   Su

TODAY'S TOP 3

▷ _____

▷ _____

▷ _____

To Do

- ☐ _____
- ☐ _____
- ☐ _____
- ☐ _____
- ☐ _____
- ☐ _____
- ☐ _____
- ☐ _____
- ☐ _____
- ☐ _____

Income Generating Activities

_____

_____

_____

_____

_____

_____

_____

_____

_____

APPOINTMENTS

6am

7am

8am

9am

10am

11am

12pm

1pm

2pm

3pm

4pm

5pm

6pm

7pm

▷ AFFIRMATIONS

▷ SALES GOALS

▷ NOTES / IDEAS

DATE   M   T   W   Th   F   Sa   Su

TODAY'S TOP 3

To Do

Income Generating Activities

- ☐
- ☐
- ☐
- ☐
- ☐
- ☐
- ☐
- ☐
- ☐
- ☐

APPOINTMENTS

6am
7am
8am
9am
10am
11am
12pm
1pm
2pm
3pm
4pm
5pm
6pm
7pm

AFFIRMATIONS

SALES GOALS

NOTES / IDEAS

DATE

M T W Th F Sa Su

▷ _____

▷ _____

▷ _____

To Do

☐ _____

☐ _____

☐ _____

☐ _____

☐ _____

☐ _____

☐ _____

☐ _____

☐ _____

☐ _____

Income Generating Activities

APPOINTMENTS

6am

7am

8am

9am

10am

11am

12pm

1pm

2pm

3pm

4pm

5pm

6pm

7pm

▷ AFFIRMATIONS

▷ SALES GOALS

▷ NOTES / IDEAS

DATE   M   T   W   Th   F   Sa   Su

TODAY'S TOP 3

To Do

- [ ]
- [ ]
- [ ]
- [ ]
- [ ]
- [ ]
- [ ]
- [ ]
- [ ]
- [ ]

Income Generating Activities

APPOINTMENTS

6am

7am

8am

9am

10am

11am

12pm

1pm

2pm

3pm

4pm

5pm

6pm

7pm

AFFIRMATIONS

SALES GOALS

NOTES / IDEAS

DATE　　　　　　　　　　　M　　T　　W　　Th　　F　　Sa　　Su

▷
▷
▷

TODAY'S TOP 3

To Do

- ☐
- ☐
- ☐
- ☐
- ☐
- ☐
- ☐
- ☐
- ☐
- ☐

Income Generating Activities

APPOINTMENTS

6am
7am
8am
9am
10am
11am
12pm
1pm
2pm
3pm
4pm
5pm
6pm
7pm

▷ AFFIRMATIONS

▷ SALES GOALS

▷ NOTES / IDEAS

DATE

M   T   W   Th   F   Sa   Su

▷ _____

▷ _____

▷ _____

TODAY'S TOP 3

To Do

- ☐ _____
- ☐ _____
- ☐ _____
- ☐ _____
- ☐ _____
- ☐ _____
- ☐ _____
- ☐ _____
- ☐ _____
- ☐ _____

Income Generating Activities

APPOINTMENTS

6am _____

7am _____

8am _____

9am _____

10am _____

11am _____

12pm _____

1pm _____

2pm _____

3pm _____

4pm _____

5pm _____

6pm _____

7pm _____

▷ AFFIRMATIONS

▷ SALES GOALS

▷ NOTES / IDEAS

DATE

M   T   W   Th   F   Sa   Su

▷ _____

▷ _____

▷ _____

To Do

- ☐ _____
- ☐ _____
- ☐ _____
- ☐ _____
- ☐ _____
- ☐ _____
- ☐ _____
- ☐ _____
- ☐ _____
- ☐ _____
- ☐ _____

Income Generating Activities

APPOINTMENTS

6am
7am
8am
9am
10am
11am
12pm
1pm
2pm
3pm
4pm
5pm
6pm
7pm

▷ AFFIRMATIONS

▷ SALES GOALS

▷ NOTES / IDEAS

THIS WEEK IN REVIEW

This Week's Big Wins

☐ _____

☐ _____

☐ _____

☐ _____

☐ _____

☐ _____

☐ _____

☐ _____

NOTES

_____

_____

_____

_____

_____

_____

NEXT WEEK AT A GLANCE

MON _____

TUE _____

WED _____

THU _____

FRI _____

SAT _____

SUN _____

DATE

M T W Th F Sa Su

▷ _____
▷ _____
▷ _____

TODAY'S TOP 3

To Do

☐ _____
☐ _____
☐ _____
☐ _____
☐ _____
☐ _____
☐ _____
☐ _____
☐ _____
☐ _____

Income Generating Activities

APPOINTMENTS

6am
7am
8am
9am
10am
11am
12pm
1pm
2pm
3pm
4pm
5pm
6pm
7pm

▷ AFFIRMATIONS

▷ SALES GOALS

▷ NOTES / IDEAS

DATE

M   T   W   Th   F   Sa   Su

TODAY'S TOP 3

To Do

- [ ]
- [ ]
- [ ]
- [ ]
- [ ]
- [ ]
- [ ]
- [ ]
- [ ]
- [ ]

Income Generating Activities

APPOINTMENTS

6am

7am

8am

9am

10am

11am

12pm

1pm

2pm

3pm

4pm

5pm

6pm

7pm

AFFIRMATIONS

SALES GOALS

NOTES / IDEAS

DATE		M	T	W	Th	F	Sa	Su

▷ _____

▷ _____

▷ _____

TODAY'S TOP 3

To Do

- ☐ _____
- ☐ _____
- ☐ _____
- ☐ _____
- ☐ _____
- ☐ _____
- ☐ _____
- ☐ _____
- ☐ _____
- ☐ _____

Income Generating Activities

APPOINTMENTS

6am	
7am	
8am	
9am	
10am	
11am	
12pm	
1pm	
2pm	
3pm	
4pm	
5pm	
6pm	
7pm	

▷ **AFFIRMATIONS**

▷ **SALES GOALS**

▷ **NOTES / IDEAS**

DATE

M   T   W   Th   F   Sa   Su

To Do

- [ ]
- [ ]
- [ ]
- [ ]
- [ ]
- [ ]
- [ ]
- [ ]
- [ ]
- [ ]

Income Generating Activities

APPOINTMENTS

6am
7am
8am
9am
10am
11am
12pm
1pm
2pm
3pm
4pm
5pm
6pm
7pm

AFFIRMATIONS

SALES GOALS

NOTES / IDEAS

DATE

M   T   W   Th   F   Sa   Su

▷ _____

▷ _____

▷ _____

TODAY'S TOP 3

To Do

- ☐ _____
- ☐ _____
- ☐ _____
- ☐ _____
- ☐ _____
- ☐ _____
- ☐ _____
- ☐ _____
- ☐ _____
- ☐ _____

Income Generating Activities

APPOINTMENTS

6am	
7am	
8am	
9am	
10am	
11am	
12pm	
1pm	
2pm	
3pm	
4pm	
5pm	
6pm	
7pm	

▷ AFFIRMATIONS

▷ SALES GOALS

▷ NOTES / IDEAS

DATE

M T W Th F Sa Su

TODAY'S TOP 3

➤ _____

➤ _____

➤ _____

To Do

☐ _____
☐ _____
☐ _____
☐ _____
☐ _____
☐ _____
☐ _____
☐ _____
☐ _____
☐ _____

Income Generating Activities

APPOINTMENTS

6am _____
7am _____
8am _____
9am _____
10am _____
11am _____
12pm _____
1pm _____
2pm _____
3pm _____
4pm _____
5pm _____
6pm _____
7pm _____

➤ AFFIRMATIONS

➤ SALES GOALS

➤ NOTES / IDEAS

▷ _____

▷ _____

▷ _____

TODAY'S TOP 3

To Do

☐ _____

☐ _____

☐ _____

☐ _____

☐ _____

☐ _____

☐ _____

☐ _____

☐ _____

☐ _____

Income Generating Activities

APPOINTMENTS

6am

7am

8am

9am

10am

11am

12pm

1pm

2pm

3pm

4pm

5pm

6pm

7pm

▷ AFFIRMATIONS

▷ SALES GOALS

▷ NOTES / IDEAS

THIS WEEK IN REVIEW

This Week's Big Wins

- [ ]
- [ ]
- [ ]
- [ ]
- [ ]
- [ ]
- [ ]
- [ ]

NOTES

NEXT WEEK AT A GLANCE

MON

TUE

WED

THU

FRI

SAT

SUN

DATE

M   T   W   Th   F   Sa   Su

▷ _____

▷ _____

▷ _____

TODAY'S TOP 3

To Do

- ☐
- ☐
- ☐
- ☐
- ☐
- ☐
- ☐
- ☐
- ☐
- ☐

Income Generating Activities

APPOINTMENTS

6am	
7am	
8am	
9am	
10am	
11am	
12pm	
1pm	
2pm	
3pm	
4pm	
5pm	
6pm	
7pm	

▷ AFFIRMATIONS

▷ SALES GOALS

▷ NOTES / IDEAS

DATE

M   T   W   Th   F   Sa   Su

TODAY'S TOP 3

- ▷ ....
- ▷ ....
- ▷ ....

To Do

- ☐ ....
- ☐ ....
- ☐ ....
- ☐ ....
- ☐ ....
- ☐ ....
- ☐ ....
- ☐ ....
- ☐ ....
- ☐ ....
- ☐ ....

Income Generating Activities

APPOINTMENTS

6am
7am
8am
9am
10am
11am
12pm
1pm
2pm
3pm
4pm
5pm
6pm
7pm

▷ AFFIRMATIONS

▷ SALES GOALS

▷ NOTES / IDEAS

DATE

M   T   W   Th   F   Sa   Su

▷ _____

▷ _____

▷ _____

TODAY'S TOP 3

To Do

☐ _____

☐ _____

☐ _____

☐ _____

☐ _____

☐ _____

☐ _____

☐ _____

☐ _____

☐ _____

Income Generating Activities

APPOINTMENTS

6am _____

7am _____

8am _____

9am _____

10am _____

11am _____

12pm _____

1pm _____

2pm _____

3pm _____

4pm _____

5pm _____

6pm _____

7pm _____

▷ AFFIRMATIONS

▷ SALES GOALS

▷ NOTES / IDEAS

DATE			M	T	W	Th	F	Sa	Su

▷ _____

▷ _____

▷ _____

TODAY'S TOP 3

To Do

☐ _____

☐ _____

☐ _____

☐ _____

☐ _____

☐ _____

☐ _____

☐ _____

☐ _____

☐ _____

Income Generating Activities

APPOINTMENTS

6am

7am

8am

9am

10am

11am

12pm

1pm

2pm

3pm

4pm

5pm

6pm

7pm

▷ AFFIRMATIONS

▷ SALES GOALS

▷ NOTES / IDEAS

DATE

M	T	W	Th	F	Sa	Su

▷ _____

▷ _____

▷ _____

TODAY'S TOP 3

To Do

- ☐ _____
- ☐ _____
- ☐ _____
- ☐ _____
- ☐ _____
- ☐ _____
- ☐ _____
- ☐ _____
- ☐ _____
- ☐ _____

Income Generating Activities

APPOINTMENTS

6am

7am

8am

9am

10am

11am

12pm

1pm

2pm

3pm

4pm

5pm

6pm

7pm

▷ AFFIRMATIONS

▷ SALES GOALS

▷ NOTES / IDEAS

DATE

M   T   W   Th   F   Sa   Su

TODAY'S TOP 3

To Do

- [ ]
- [ ]
- [ ]
- [ ]
- [ ]
- [ ]
- [ ]
- [ ]
- [ ]
- [ ]

Income Generating Activities

APPOINTMENTS

6am

7am

8am

9am

10am

11am

12pm

1pm

2pm

3pm

4pm

5pm

6pm

7pm

AFFIRMATIONS

SALES GOALS

NOTES / IDEAS

DATE

M　T　W　Th　F　Sa　Su

▷ _____

▷ _____

▷ _____

TODAY'S TOP 3

To Do

☐ _____
☐ _____
☐ _____
☐ _____
☐ _____
☐ _____
☐ _____
☐ _____
☐ _____

Income Generating Activities

_____
_____
_____
_____
_____
_____
_____
_____
_____

APPOINTMENTS

6am

7am

8am

9am

10am

11am

12pm

1pm

2pm

3pm

4pm

5pm

6pm

7pm

▷ AFFIRMATIONS

▷ SALES GOALS

▷ NOTES / IDEAS

THIS WEEK IN REVIEW

This Week's Big Wins

- [ ]
- [ ]
- [ ]
- [ ]
- [ ]
- [ ]
- [ ]
- [ ]

NOTES

NEXT WEEK AT A GLANCE

MON

TUE

WED

THU

FRI

SAT

SUN

DATE

M   T   W   Th   F   Sa   Su

>
>
>

TODAY'S TOP 3

To Do

- [ ]
- [ ]
- [ ]
- [ ]
- [ ]
- [ ]
- [ ]
- [ ]
- [ ]
- [ ]

Income Generating Activities

APPOINTMENTS

6am
7am
8am
9am
10am
11am
12pm
1pm
2pm
3pm
4pm
5pm
6pm
7pm

> AFFIRMATIONS

> SALES GOALS

> NOTES / IDEAS

DATE

M T W Th F Sa Su

TODAY'S TOP 3

▷ _____

▷ _____

▷ _____

To Do

- ☐ _____
- ☐ _____
- ☐ _____
- ☐ _____
- ☐ _____
- ☐ _____
- ☐ _____
- ☐ _____
- ☐ _____
- ☐ _____

Income Generating Activities

APPOINTMENTS

6am

7am

8am

9am

10am

11am

12pm

1pm

2pm

3pm

4pm

5pm

6pm

7pm

▷ AFFIRMATIONS

▷ SALES GOALS

▷ NOTES / IDEAS

DATE

M T W Th F Sa Su

▷ _____
▷ _____
▷ _____
▷ _____

To Do

☐ _____
☐ _____
☐ _____
☐ _____
☐ _____
☐ _____
☐ _____
☐ _____
☐ _____
☐ _____

Income Generating Activities

APPOINTMENTS

6am
7am
8am
9am
10am
11am
12pm
1pm
2pm
3pm
4pm
5pm
6pm
7pm

▷ AFFIRMATIONS

▷ SALES GOALS

▷ NOTES / IDEAS

DATE

M   T   W   Th   F   Sa   Su

TODAY'S TOP 3

To Do

- [ ]
- [ ]
- [ ]
- [ ]
- [ ]
- [ ]
- [ ]
- [ ]
- [ ]
- [ ]

Income Generating Activities

APPOINTMENTS

6am

7am

8am

9am

10am

11am

12pm

1pm

2pm

3pm

4pm

5pm

6pm

7pm

AFFIRMATIONS

SALES GOALS

NOTES / IDEAS

DATE

M   T   W   Th   F   Sa   Su

TODAY'S TOP 3

To Do

- ☐
- ☐
- ☐
- ☐
- ☐
- ☐
- ☐
- ☐
- ☐
- ☐

Income Generating Activities

APPOINTMENTS

6am	
7am	
8am	
9am	
10am	
11am	
12pm	
1pm	
2pm	
3pm	
4pm	
5pm	
6pm	
7pm	

AFFIRMATIONS

SALES GOALS

NOTES / IDEAS

DATE

M   T   W   Th   F   Sa   Su

TODAY'S TOP 3

To Do

- [ ]
- [ ]
- [ ]
- [ ]
- [ ]
- [ ]
- [ ]
- [ ]
- [ ]
- [ ]
- [ ]

Income Generating Activities

APPOINTMENTS

6am
7am
8am
9am
10am
11am
12pm
1pm
2pm
3pm
4pm
5pm
6pm
7pm

AFFIRMATIONS

SALES GOALS

NOTES / IDEAS

DATE

▶

▶

▶

TODAY'S TOP 3

To Do

☐

☐

☐

☐

☐

☐

☐

☐

☐

☐

Income Generating Activities

APPOINTMENTS

6am	
7am	
8am	
9am	
10am	
11am	
12pm	
1pm	
2pm	
3pm	
4pm	
5pm	
6pm	
7pm	

▶ AFFIRMATIONS

▶ SALES GOALS

▶ NOTES / IDEAS

THIS WEEK IN REVIEW

This Week's Big Wins

- [ ]
- [ ]
- [ ]
- [ ]
- [ ]
- [ ]
- [ ]
- [ ]

NOTES

NEXT WEEK AT A GLANCE

MON

TUE

WED

THU

FRI

SAT

SUN

_____ MONTH IN REVIEW

MONTHLY WINS

▷
▷
▷
▷

▷
▷
▷
▷

INCOME GENERATING HABITS THAT SUPPORT MONTHLY GOALS

▷ ☐ DAILY HABIT ☐ WEEKLY HABIT

▷ ☐ DAILY HABIT ☐ WEEKLY HABIT

▷ ☐ DAILY HABIT ☐ WEEKLY HABIT

▷ ☐ DAILY HABIT ☐ WEEKLY HABIT

▷ ☐ DAILY HABIT ☐ WEEKLY HABIT

DAILY SALES

1.	11.	21.
2.	12.	22.
3.	13.	23.
4.	14.	24.
5.	15.	25.
6.	16.	26.
7.	17.	27.
8.	18.	28.
9.	19.	29.
10.	20.	30.

▷ *Create Your Future*

Dream Big, Set Goals, Take Action

MONTH _____

SUNDAY	MONDAY	TUESDAY	WEDNESDAY

Goals are dreams with deadlines.

THURSDAY	FRIDAY	SATURDAY	NOTES
			_____
			_____
			_____
			_____
			_____
			_____
			_____
			_____
			_____
			_____
			_____
			_____
			_____
			_____
			_____
			_____
			_____
			_____
			_____
			_____
			_____
			_____

DATE

M T W Th F Sa Su

▷ _____

▷ _____

▷ _____

To Do

☐ _____

☐ _____

☐ _____

☐ _____

☐ _____

☐ _____

☐ _____

☐ _____

☐ _____

☐ _____

Income Generating Activities

APPOINTMENTS

6am

7am

8am

9am

10am

11am

12pm

1pm

2pm

3pm

4pm

5pm

6pm

7pm

▷ AFFIRMATIONS

▷ SALES GOALS

▷ NOTES / IDEAS

DATE

M   T   W   Th   F   Sa   Su

TODAY'S TOP 3

▷ _____
▷ _____
▷ _____

To Do

☐ _____
☐ _____
☐ _____
☐ _____
☐ _____
☐ _____
☐ _____
☐ _____
☐ _____
☐ _____

Income Generating Activities

APPOINTMENTS

6am
7am
8am
9am
10am
11am
12pm
1pm
2pm
3pm
4pm
5pm
6pm
7pm

▷ AFFIRMATIONS

▷ SALES GOALS

▷ NOTES / IDEAS

DATE

M   T   W   Th   F   Sa   Su

TODAY'S TOP 3

To Do

☐
☐
☐
☐
☐
☐
☐
☐
☐
☐

Income Generating Activities

APPOINTMENTS

6am

7am

8am   ⟩ AFFIRMATIONS

9am

10am

11am   ⟩ SALES GOALS

12pm

1pm

2pm

3pm

4pm   ⟩ NOTES / IDEAS

5pm

6pm

7pm

DATE

M T W Th F Sa Su

To Do

- [ ]
- [ ]
- [ ]
- [ ]
- [ ]
- [ ]
- [ ]
- [ ]
- [ ]
- [ ]

Income Generating Activities

APPOINTMENTS

6am

7am

8am

9am

10am

11am

12pm

1pm

2pm

3pm

4pm

5pm

6pm

7pm

AFFIRMATIONS

SALES GOALS

NOTES / IDEAS

DATE

M   T   W   Th   F   Sa   Su

▷ _____

▷ _____

▷ _____

TODAY'S TOP 3

To Do

- ☐ _____
- ☐ _____
- ☐ _____
- ☐ _____
- ☐ _____
- ☐ _____
- ☐ _____
- ☐ _____
- ☐ _____
- ☐ _____

Income Generating Activities

APPOINTMENTS

6am _____

7am _____

8am _____

9am _____

10am _____

11am _____

12pm _____

1pm _____

2pm _____

3pm _____

4pm _____

5pm _____

6pm _____

7pm _____

▷ AFFIRMATIONS

▷ SALES GOALS

▷ NOTES / IDEAS

DATE

M   T   W   Th   F   Sa   Su

▷ _____

▷ _____

▷ _____

To Do

☐ _____

☐ _____

☐ _____

☐ _____

☐ _____

☐ _____

☐ _____

☐ _____

☐ _____

☐ _____

Income Generating Activities

APPOINTMENTS

6am

7am

8am

9am

10am

11am

12pm

1pm

2pm

3pm

4pm

5pm

6pm

7pm

▷ AFFIRMATIONS

▷ SALES GOALS

▷ NOTES / IDEAS

DATE

M   T   W   Th   F   Sa   Su

TODAY'S TOP 3

To Do

- [ ]
- [ ]
- [ ]
- [ ]
- [ ]
- [ ]
- [ ]
- [ ]
- [ ]
- [ ]

Income Generating Activities

APPOINTMENTS

6am
7am
8am
9am
10am
11am
12pm
1pm
2pm
3pm
4pm
5pm
6pm
7pm

AFFIRMATIONS

SALES GOALS

NOTES / IDEAS

THIS WEEK IN REVIEW

This Week's Big Wins

- ☐ _____
- ☐ _____
- ☐ _____
- ☐ _____
- ☐ _____
- ☐ _____
- ☐ _____

NOTES

_____

_____

_____

_____

_____

_____

_____

NEXT WEEK AT A GLANCE

MON _____

TUE _____

WED _____

THU _____

FRI _____

SAT _____

SUN _____

DATE

M T W Th F Sa Su

TODAY'S TOP 3

▷ _____

▷ _____

▷ _____

To Do

- ☐
- ☐
- ☐
- ☐
- ☐
- ☐
- ☐
- ☐
- ☐
- ☐

Income Generating Activities

APPOINTMENTS

6am

7am

8am

9am

10am

11am

12pm

1pm

2pm

3pm

4pm

5pm

6pm

7pm

▷ AFFIRMATIONS

▷ SALES GOALS

▷ NOTES / IDEAS

DATE			M	T	W	Th	F	Sa	Su

▷ _____

▷ _____

▷ _____

TODAY'S TOP 3

To Do

☐ _____

☐ _____

☐ _____

☐ _____

☐ _____

☐ _____

☐ _____

☐ _____

☐ _____

☐ _____

Income Generating Activities

APPOINTMENTS

6am

7am

8am

9am

10am

11am

12pm

1pm

2pm

3pm

4pm

5pm

6pm

7pm

▷ AFFIRMATIONS

▷ SALES GOALS

▷ NOTES / IDEAS

DATE

M T W Th F Sa Su

TODAY'S TOP 3

To Do

- ☐
- ☐
- ☐
- ☐
- ☐
- ☐
- ☐
- ☐
- ☐
- ☐

Income Generating Activities

APPOINTMENTS

6am

7am

8am

9am

10am

11am

12pm

1pm

2pm

3pm

4pm

5pm

6pm

7pm

AFFIRMATIONS

SALES GOALS

NOTES / IDEAS

DATE

M   T   W   Th   F   Sa   Su

▷
▷
▷

TODAY'S TOP 3

To Do

☐
☐
☐
☐
☐
☐
☐
☐
☐
☐

Income Generating Activities

APPOINTMENTS

6am
7am
8am
9am
10am
11am
12pm
1pm
2pm
3pm
4pm
5pm
6pm
7pm

▷ AFFIRMATIONS

▷ SALES GOALS

▷ NOTES / IDEAS

DATE

M	T	W	Th	F	Sa	Su

▷ _____

▷ _____

▷ _____

TODAY'S TOP 3

To Do

- ☐ _____
- ☐ _____
- ☐ _____
- ☐ _____
- ☐ _____
- ☐ _____
- ☐ _____
- ☐ _____
- ☐ _____
- ☐ _____
- ☐ _____

Income Generating Activities

APPOINTMENTS

6am	
7am	
8am	
9am	
10am	
11am	
12pm	
1pm	
2pm	
3pm	
4pm	
5pm	
6pm	
7pm	

▷ AFFIRMATIONS

▷ SALES GOALS

▷ NOTES / IDEAS

DATE

M   T   W   Th   F   Sa   Su

TODAY'S TOP 3

To Do

- [ ]
- [ ]
- [ ]
- [ ]
- [ ]
- [ ]
- [ ]
- [ ]
- [ ]
- [ ]

Income Generating Activities

APPOINTMENTS

6am	
7am	
8am	
9am	
10am	
11am	
12pm	
1pm	
2pm	
3pm	
4pm	
5pm	
6pm	
7pm	

AFFIRMATIONS

SALES GOALS

NOTES / IDEAS

DATE

M   T   W   Th   F   Sa   Su

▷ _____

▷ _____

▷ _____

TODAY'S TOP 3

To Do

- ☐ _____
- ☐ _____
- ☐ _____
- ☐ _____
- ☐ _____
- ☐ _____
- ☐ _____
- ☐ _____
- ☐ _____
- ☐ _____

Income Generating Activities

APPOINTMENTS

6am _____

7am _____

8am _____

9am _____

10am _____

11am _____

12pm _____

1pm _____

2pm _____

3pm _____

4pm _____

5pm _____

6pm _____

7pm _____

▷ AFFIRMATIONS

▷ SALES GOALS

▷ NOTES / IDEAS

THIS WEEK IN REVIEW

This Week's Big Wins

- [ ]
- [ ]
- [ ]
- [ ]
- [ ]
- [ ]
- [ ]

NOTES

NEXT WEEK AT A GLANCE

MON

TUE

WED

THU

FRI

SAT

SUN

DATE   M   T   W   Th   F   Sa   Su

▷ _____

▷ _____

▷ _____

To Do

☐ _____
☐ _____
☐ _____
☐ _____
☐ _____
☐ _____
☐ _____
☐ _____
☐ _____
☐ _____

Income Generating Activities

APPOINTMENTS

6am _____
7am _____
8am _____
9am _____
10am _____
11am _____
12pm _____
1pm _____
2pm _____
3pm _____
4pm _____
5pm _____
6pm _____
7pm _____

▷ AFFIRMATIONS

▷ SALES GOALS

▷ NOTES / IDEAS

DATE

	M	T	W	Th	F	Sa	Su

▷ _____

▷ _____

▷ _____

To Do

☐ _____

☐ _____

☐ _____

☐ _____

☐ _____

☐ _____

☐ _____

☐ _____

☐ _____

☐ _____

Income Generating Activities

APPOINTMENTS

6am

7am

8am

9am

10am

11am

12pm

1pm

2pm

3pm

4pm

5pm

6pm

7pm

▷ AFFIRMATIONS

▷ SALES GOALS

▷ NOTES / IDEAS

DATE

M	T	W	Th	F	Sa	Su

▷ _____

▷ _____

▷ _____

To Do

☐ _____

☐ _____

☐ _____

☐ _____

☐ _____

☐ _____

☐ _____

☐ _____

☐ _____

☐ _____

Income Generating Activities

APPOINTMENTS

6am

7am

8am

9am

10am

11am

12pm

1pm

2pm

3pm

4pm

5pm

6pm

7pm

▷ AFFIRMATIONS

▷ SALES GOALS

▷ NOTES / IDEAS

DATE

M   T   W   Th   F   Sa   Su

TODAY'S TOP 3

To Do

- ☐
- ☐
- ☐
- ☐
- ☐
- ☐
- ☐
- ☐
- ☐
- ☐

Income Generating Activities

APPOINTMENTS

6am	
7am	
8am	
9am	
10am	
11am	
12pm	
1pm	
2pm	
3pm	
4pm	
5pm	
6pm	
7pm	

AFFIRMATIONS

SALES GOALS

NOTES / IDEAS

DATE

M T W Th F Sa Su

▷ _____

▷ _____

▷ _____

TODAY'S TOP 3

To Do

☐ _____

☐ _____

☐ _____

☐ _____

☐ _____

☐ _____

☐ _____

☐ _____

☐ _____

☐ _____

Income Generating Activities

_____

_____

_____

_____

_____

_____

_____

_____

APPOINTMENTS

6am

7am

8am

9am

10am

11am

12pm

1pm

2pm

3pm

4pm

5pm

6pm

7pm

▷ AFFIRMATIONS

▷ SALES GOALS

▷ NOTES / IDEAS

DATE

M   T   W   Th   F   Sa   Su

TODAY'S TOP 3

To Do

- [ ]
- [ ]
- [ ]
- [ ]
- [ ]
- [ ]
- [ ]
- [ ]
- [ ]
- [ ]

Income Generating Activities

APPOINTMENTS

6am

7am

8am

9am

10am

11am

12pm

1pm

2pm

3pm

4pm

5pm

6pm

7pm

AFFIRMATIONS

SALES GOALS

NOTES / IDEAS

DATE

M   T   W   Th   F   Sa   Su

➤
➤
➤

To Do

☐
☐
☐
☐
☐
☐
☐
☐
☐
☐

Income Generating Activities

APPOINTMENTS

6am
7am
8am
9am
10am
11am
12pm
1pm
2pm
3pm
4pm
5pm
6pm
7pm

➤ **AFFIRMATIONS**

➤ **SALES GOALS**

➤ **NOTES / IDEAS**

THIS WEEK IN REVIEW

This Week's Big Wins

- [ ]
- [ ]
- [ ]
- [ ]
- [ ]
- [ ]
- [ ]

NOTES

NEXT WEEK AT A GLANCE

MON

TUE

WED

THU

FRI

SAT

SUN

DATE

M T W Th F Sa Su

▷ _____
▷ _____
▷ _____

TODAY'S TOP 3

To Do

☐ _____
☐ _____
☐ _____
☐ _____
☐ _____
☐ _____
☐ _____
☐ _____
☐ _____
☐ _____

Income Generating Activities

APPOINTMENTS

6am
7am
8am
9am
10am
11am
12pm
1pm
2pm
3pm
4pm
5pm
6pm
7pm

▷ AFFIRMATIONS

▷ SALES GOALS

▷ NOTES / IDEAS

DATE

M T W Th F Sa Su

▷

▷

▷

TODAY'S TOP 3

To Do

☐

☐

☐

☐

☐

☐

☐

☐

☐

☐

Income Generating Activities

APPOINTMENTS

6am

7am

8am

9am

10am

11am

12pm

1pm

2pm

3pm

4pm

5pm

6pm

7pm

▷ AFFIRMATIONS

▷ SALES GOALS

▷ NOTES / IDEAS

DATE   M   T   W   Th   F   Sa   Su

▷ _____
▷ _____
▷ _____

To Do

☐ _____
☐ _____
☐ _____
☐ _____
☐ _____
☐ _____
☐ _____
☐ _____
☐ _____
☐ _____

Income Generating Activities

APPOINTMENTS

6am _____
7am _____
8am _____
9am _____
10am _____
11am _____
12pm _____
1pm _____
2pm _____
3pm _____
4pm _____
5pm _____
6pm _____
7pm _____

▷ AFFIRMATIONS

▷ SALES GOALS

▷ NOTES / IDEAS

DATE		M	T	W	Th	F	Sa	Su

▷ _____

▷ _____

▷ _____

TODAY'S TOP 3

To Do

- ☐ _____
- ☐ _____
- ☐ _____
- ☐ _____
- ☐ _____
- ☐ _____
- ☐ _____
- ☐ _____
- ☐ _____
- ☐ _____
- ☐ _____

Income Generating Activities

APPOINTMENTS

6am

7am

8am

9am

10am

11am

12pm

1pm

2pm

3pm

4pm

5pm

6pm

7pm

▷ AFFIRMATIONS

▷ SALES GOALS

▷ NOTES / IDEAS

DATE

M   T   W   Th   F   Sa   Su

▷
▷
▷

TODAY'S TOP 3

To Do

- ☐
- ☐
- ☐
- ☐
- ☐
- ☐
- ☐
- ☐
- ☐
- ☐

Income Generating Activities

APPOINTMENTS

6am
7am
8am
9am
10am
11am
12pm
1pm
2pm
3pm
4pm
5pm
6pm
7pm

▷ **AFFIRMATIONS**

▷ **SALES GOALS**

▷ **NOTES / IDEAS**

DATE

M   T   W   Th   F   Sa   Su

TODAY'S TOP 3

To Do

- [ ]
- [ ]
- [ ]
- [ ]
- [ ]
- [ ]
- [ ]
- [ ]
- [ ]
- [ ]
- [ ]

Income Generating Activities

APPOINTMENTS

6am

7am

8am

9am

10am

11am

12pm

1pm

2pm

3pm

4pm

5pm

6pm

7pm

AFFIRMATIONS

SALES GOALS

NOTES / IDEAS

DATE

M   T   W   Th   F   Sa   Su

To Do

- ☐
- ☐
- ☐
- ☐
- ☐
- ☐
- ☐
- ☐
- ☐
- ☐

Income Generating Activities

APPOINTMENTS

6am

7am

8am

9am

10am

11am

12pm

1pm

2pm

3pm

4pm

5pm

6pm

7pm

AFFIRMATIONS

SALES GOALS

NOTES / IDEAS

THIS WEEK IN REVIEW

This Week's Big Wins

- ☐
- ☐
- ☐
- ☐
- ☐
- ☐
- ☐

NOTES

NEXT WEEK AT A GLANCE

MON

TUE

WED

THU

FRI

SAT

SUN

DATE

M   T   W   Th   F   Sa   Su

▷ _____

▷ _____

▷ _____

TODAY'S TOP 3

To Do

- ☐ _____
- ☐ _____
- ☐ _____
- ☐ _____
- ☐ _____
- ☐ _____
- ☐ _____
- ☐ _____
- ☐ _____
- ☐ _____

Income Generating Activities

_____

_____

_____

_____

_____

_____

_____

_____

_____

APPOINTMENTS

6am

7am

8am

9am

10am

11am

12pm

1pm

2pm

3pm

4pm

5pm

6pm

7pm

▷ AFFIRMATIONS

▷ SALES GOALS

▷ NOTES / IDEAS

DATE

M   T   W   Th   F   Sa   Su

TODAY'S TOP 3

To Do

- [ ]
- [ ]
- [ ]
- [ ]
- [ ]
- [ ]
- [ ]
- [ ]
- [ ]
- [ ]
- [ ]

Income Generating Activities

APPOINTMENTS

6am

7am

8am

9am

10am

11am

12pm

1pm

2pm

3pm

4pm

5pm

6pm

7pm

AFFIRMATIONS

SALES GOALS

NOTES / IDEAS

DATE

M   T   W   Th   F   Sa   Su

▷ _____

▷ _____

▷ _____

To Do

☐ _____

☐ _____

☐ _____

☐ _____

☐ _____

☐ _____

☐ _____

☐ _____

☐ _____

☐ _____

Income Generating Activities

APPOINTMENTS

6am

7am

8am

9am

10am

11am

12pm

1pm

2pm

3pm

4pm

5pm

6pm

7pm

▷ AFFIRMATIONS

▷ SALES GOALS

▷ NOTES / IDEAS

DATE

M   T   W   Th   F   Sa   Su

TODAY'S TOP 3

To Do

- ☐
- ☐
- ☐
- ☐
- ☐
- ☐
- ☐
- ☐
- ☐
- ☐

Income Generating Activities

APPOINTMENTS

6am

7am

8am

9am

10am

11am

12pm

1pm

2pm

3pm

4pm

5pm

6pm

7pm

AFFIRMATIONS

SALES GOALS

NOTES / IDEAS

DATE

M   T   W   Th   F   Sa   Su

▷ _____

▷ _____

▷ _____

TODAY'S TOP 3

To Do

- ☐ _____
- ☐ _____
- ☐ _____
- ☐ _____
- ☐ _____
- ☐ _____
- ☐ _____
- ☐ _____
- ☐ _____
- ☐ _____
- ☐ _____

Income Generating Activities

APPOINTMENTS

6am

7am

8am

9am

10am

11am

12pm

1pm

2pm

3pm

4pm

5pm

6pm

7pm

▷ AFFIRMATIONS

▷ SALES GOALS

▷ NOTES / IDEAS

DATE

M   T   W   Th   F   Sa   Su

▷ _____

▷ _____

▷ _____

TODAY'S TOP 3

To Do

- ☐ _____
- ☐ _____
- ☐ _____
- ☐ _____
- ☐ _____
- ☐ _____
- ☐ _____
- ☐ _____
- ☐ _____
- ☐ _____

Income Generating Activities

APPOINTMENTS

6am _____

7am _____

8am _____

9am _____

10am _____

11am _____

12pm _____

1pm _____

2pm _____

3pm _____

4pm _____

5pm _____

6pm _____

7pm _____

▷ AFFIRMATIONS

▷ SALES GOALS

▷ NOTES / IDEAS

DATE

M   T   W   Th   F   Sa   Su

▷ _____

▷ _____

▷ _____

TODAY'S TOP 3

To Do

- ☐ _____
- ☐ _____
- ☐ _____
- ☐ _____
- ☐ _____
- ☐ _____
- ☐ _____
- ☐ _____
- ☐ _____
- ☐ _____
- ☐ _____

Income Generating Activities

APPOINTMENTS

6am

7am

8am

9am

10am

11am

12pm

1pm

2pm

3pm

4pm

5pm

6pm

7pm

▷ AFFIRMATIONS

▷ SALES GOALS

▷ NOTES / IDEAS

THIS WEEK IN REVIEW
This Week's Big Wins

☐ _____

☐ _____

☐ _____

☐ _____

☐ _____

☐ _____

☐ _____

☐ _____

NOTES

_____

_____

_____

_____

_____

_____

NEXT WEEK AT A GLANCE

MON _____

TUE _____

WED _____

THU _____

FRI _____

SAT _____

SUN _____

_____ MONTH IN REVIEW

MONTHLY WINS

▷
▷
▷
▷

▷
▷
▷
▷

INCOME GENERATING HABITS THAT SUPPORT MONTHLY GOALS

▷   ☐ DAILY HABIT   ☐ WEEKLY HABIT

▷   ☐ DAILY HABIT   ☐ WEEKLY HABIT

▷   ☐ DAILY HABIT   ☐ WEEKLY HABIT

▷   ☐ DAILY HABIT   ☐ WEEKLY HABIT

▷   ☐ DAILY HABIT   ☐ WEEKLY HABIT

DAILY SALES

1.	11.	21.
2.	12.	22.
3.	13.	23.
4.	14.	24.
5.	15.	25.
6.	16.	26.
7.	17.	27.
8.	18.	28.
9.	19.	29.
10.	20.	30.

▷ *A goal without a plan is a wish.*

Follow Your Dreams

MONTH _____

SUNDAY	MONDAY	TUESDAY	WEDNESDAY

Selling is the world's highest paid profession.
– *Earl Nightingale*

THURSDAY	FRIDAY	SATURDAY

NOTES

_____
_____
_____
_____
_____
_____
_____
_____
_____
_____
_____
_____
_____
_____
_____
_____
_____
_____
_____
_____
_____
_____
_____
_____
_____
_____
_____
_____

DATE

M T W Th F Sa Su

⟫ _____

⟫ _____

⟫ _____

To Do

- ☐ _____
- ☐ _____
- ☐ _____
- ☐ _____
- ☐ _____
- ☐ _____
- ☐ _____
- ☐ _____
- ☐ _____
- ☐ _____
- ☐ _____

Income Generating Activities

APPOINTMENTS

6am	
7am	
8am	
9am	
10am	
11am	
12pm	
1pm	
2pm	
3pm	
4pm	
5pm	
6pm	
7pm	

⟫ AFFIRMATIONS

⟫ SALES GOALS

⟫ NOTES / IDEAS

DATE

M   T   W   Th   F   Sa   Su

TODAY'S TOP 3

To Do

Income Generating Activities

APPOINTMENTS

6am

7am

8am

9am

10am

11am

12pm

1pm

2pm

3pm

4pm

5pm

6pm

7pm

AFFIRMATIONS

SALES GOALS

NOTES / IDEAS

DATE

M   T   W   Th   F   Sa   Su

▷ _____

▷ _____

▷ _____

TODAY'S TOP 3

To Do

- ☐ _____
- ☐ _____
- ☐ _____
- ☐ _____
- ☐ _____
- ☐ _____
- ☐ _____
- ☐ _____
- ☐ _____
- ☐ _____
- ☐ _____

Income Generating Activities

APPOINTMENTS

6am	
7am	
8am	
9am	
10am	
11am	
12pm	
1pm	
2pm	
3pm	
4pm	
5pm	
6pm	
7pm	

▷ AFFIRMATIONS

▷ SALES GOALS

▷ NOTES / IDEAS

DATE

M T W Th F Sa Su

TODAY'S TOP 3

▷ _____

▷ _____

▷ _____

To Do

- ☐
- ☐
- ☐
- ☐
- ☐
- ☐
- ☐
- ☐
- ☐
- ☐

Income Generating Activities

APPOINTMENTS

6am

7am

8am

9am

10am

11am

12pm

1pm

2pm

3pm

4pm

5pm

6pm

7pm

▷ AFFIRMATIONS

▷ SALES GOALS

▷ NOTES / IDEAS

DATE

M   T   W   Th   F   Sa   Su

▷ ....

▷ ....

▷ ....

To Do

☐ ....

☐ ....

☐ ....

☐ ....

☐ ....

☐ ....

☐ ....

☐ ....

☐ ....

☐ ....

Income Generating Activities

APPOINTMENTS

6am

7am

8am

9am

10am

11am

12pm

1pm

2pm

3pm

4pm

5pm

6pm

7pm

▷ AFFIRMATIONS

▷ SALES GOALS

▷ NOTES / IDEAS

DATE

M   T   W   Th   F   Sa   Su

To Do

- ☐
- ☐
- ☐
- ☐
- ☐
- ☐
- ☐
- ☐
- ☐
- ☐

Income Generating Activities

APPOINTMENTS

6am
7am
8am
9am
10am
11am
12pm
1pm
2pm
3pm
4pm
5pm
6pm
7pm

AFFIRMATIONS

SALES GOALS

NOTES / IDEAS

DATE   M   T   W   Th   F   Sa   Su

▷

▷

▷

TODAY'S TOP 3

To Do

- ☐
- ☐
- ☐
- ☐
- ☐
- ☐
- ☐
- ☐
- ☐
- ☐
- ☐

Income Generating Activities

APPOINTMENTS

6am

7am

8am

9am

10am

11am

12pm

1pm

2pm

3pm

4pm

5pm

6pm

7pm

▷ AFFIRMATIONS

▷ SALES GOALS

▷ NOTES / IDEAS

THIS WEEK IN REVIEW

This Week's Big Wins

- [ ]
- [ ]
- [ ]
- [ ]
- [ ]
- [ ]
- [ ]

NOTES

NEXT WEEK AT A GLANCE

MON

TUE

WED

THU

FRI

SAT

SUN

DATE

M   T   W   Th   F   Sa   Su

▷
▷
▷

TODAY'S TOP 3

To Do

- ☐
- ☐
- ☐
- ☐
- ☐
- ☐
- ☐
- ☐
- ☐
- ☐
- ☐

Income Generating Activities

APPOINTMENTS

6am
7am
8am
9am
10am
11am
12pm
1pm
2pm
3pm
4pm
5pm
6pm
7pm

▷ AFFIRMATIONS

▷ SALES GOALS

▷ NOTES / IDEAS

DATE

M   T   W   Th   F   Sa   Su

TODAY'S TOP 3

To Do

- [ ]
- [ ]
- [ ]
- [ ]
- [ ]
- [ ]
- [ ]
- [ ]
- [ ]
- [ ]

Income Generating Activities

APPOINTMENTS

6am
7am
8am
9am
10am
11am
12pm
1pm
2pm
3pm
4pm
5pm
6pm
7pm

AFFIRMATIONS

SALES GOALS

NOTES / IDEAS

DATE

M   T   W   Th   F   Sa   Su

➤

➤

➤

To Do

☐
☐
☐
☐
☐
☐
☐
☐
☐
☐
☐

Income Generating Activities

APPOINTMENTS

6am
7am
8am
9am
10am
11am
12pm
1pm
2pm
3pm
4pm
5pm
6pm
7pm

➤ AFFIRMATIONS

➤ SALES GOALS

➤ NOTES / IDEAS

DATE   M   T   W   Th   F   Sa   Su

▷ _____

▷ _____

▷ _____

TODAY'S TOP 3

To Do

☐ _____
☐ _____
☐ _____
☐ _____
☐ _____
☐ _____
☐ _____
☐ _____
☐ _____
☐ _____

Income Generating Activities

APPOINTMENTS

6am _____
7am _____
8am _____
9am _____
10am _____
11am _____
12pm _____
1pm _____
2pm _____
3pm _____
4pm _____
5pm _____
6pm _____
7pm _____

▷ AFFIRMATIONS

▷ SALES GOALS

▷ NOTES / IDEAS

DATE

M T W Th F Sa Su

▷
▷
▷

To Do

- ☐
- ☐
- ☐
- ☐
- ☐
- ☐
- ☐
- ☐
- ☐
- ☐

Income Generating Activities

APPOINTMENTS

6am
7am
8am
9am
10am
11am
12pm
1pm
2pm
3pm
4pm
5pm
6pm
7pm

▷ AFFIRMATIONS

▷ SALES GOALS

▷ NOTES / IDEAS

DATE

M　T　W　Th　F　Sa　Su

▷ _____

▷ _____

▷ _____

TODAY'S TOP 3

To Do

- ☐ _____
- ☐ _____
- ☐ _____
- ☐ _____
- ☐ _____
- ☐ _____
- ☐ _____
- ☐ _____
- ☐ _____
- ☐ _____

Income Generating Activities

APPOINTMENTS

6am

7am

8am

9am

10am

11am

12pm

1pm

2pm

3pm

4pm

5pm

6pm

7pm

▷ AFFIRMATIONS

▷ SALES GOALS

▷ NOTES / IDEAS

DATE

M T W Th F Sa Su

▷ ....

▷ ....

▷ ....

TODAY'S TOP 3

To Do

- ☐ ....
- ☐ ....
- ☐ ....
- ☐ ....
- ☐ ....
- ☐ ....
- ☐ ....
- ☐ ....
- ☐ ....
- ☐ ....
- ☐ ....

Income Generating Activities

APPOINTMENTS

6am ....

7am ....

8am ....

9am ....

10am ....

11am ....

12pm ....

1pm ....

2pm ....

3pm ....

4pm ....

5pm ....

6pm ....

7pm ....

▷ AFFIRMATIONS

▷ SALES GOALS

▷ NOTES / IDEAS

THIS WEEK IN REVIEW

This Week's Big Wins

☐ _____

☐ _____

☐ _____

☐ _____

☐ _____

☐ _____

☐ _____

NOTES

_____

_____

_____

_____

_____

_____

_____

NEXT WEEK AT A GLANCE

MON _____

TUE _____

WED _____

THU _____

FRI _____

SAT _____

SUN _____

DATE

M T W Th F Sa Su

TODAY'S TOP 3

To Do

- [ ]
- [ ]
- [ ]
- [ ]
- [ ]
- [ ]
- [ ]
- [ ]
- [ ]
- [ ]

Income Generating Activities

APPOINTMENTS

6am

7am

8am

9am

10am

11am

12pm

1pm

2pm

3pm

4pm

5pm

6pm

7pm

AFFIRMATIONS

SALES GOALS

NOTES / IDEAS

DATE

M   T   W   Th   F   Sa   Su

TODAY'S TOP 3

To Do

- [ ]
- [ ]
- [ ]
- [ ]
- [ ]
- [ ]
- [ ]
- [ ]
- [ ]
- [ ]

Income Generating Activities

APPOINTMENTS

6am

7am

8am

9am

10am

11am

12pm

1pm

2pm

3pm

4pm

5pm

6pm

7pm

AFFIRMATIONS

SALES GOALS

NOTES / IDEAS

DATE

M   T   W   Th   F   Sa   Su

▶ ....

▶ ....

▶ ....

To Do

- ☐ ....
- ☐ ....
- ☐ ....
- ☐ ....
- ☐ ....
- ☐ ....
- ☐ ....
- ☐ ....
- ☐ ....
- ☐ ....

Income Generating Activities

APPOINTMENTS

6am

7am

8am

9am

10am

11am

12pm

1pm

2pm

3pm

4pm

5pm

6pm

7pm

▶ AFFIRMATIONS

▶ SALES GOALS

▶ NOTES / IDEAS

DATE

M   T   W   Th   F   Sa   Su

▷ _____

▷ _____

▷ _____

TODAY'S TOP 3

To Do

☐ _____
☐ _____
☐ _____
☐ _____
☐ _____
☐ _____
☐ _____
☐ _____
☐ _____
☐ _____

Income Generating Activities

APPOINTMENTS

6am _____
7am _____
8am _____
9am _____
10am _____
11am _____
12pm _____
1pm _____
2pm _____
3pm _____
4pm _____
5pm _____
6pm _____
7pm _____

▷ AFFIRMATIONS

▷ SALES GOALS

▷ NOTES / IDEAS

DATE

M   T   W   Th   F   Sa   Su

▷ _____

▷ _____

▷ _____

TODAY'S TOP 3

To Do

- ☐ _____
- ☐ _____
- ☐ _____
- ☐ _____
- ☐ _____
- ☐ _____
- ☐ _____
- ☐ _____
- ☐ _____
- ☐ _____
- ☐ _____

Income Generating Activities

APPOINTMENTS

6am

7am

8am

9am

10am

11am

12pm

1pm

2pm

3pm

4pm

5pm

6pm

7pm

▷ AFFIRMATIONS

▷ SALES GOALS

▷ NOTES / IDEAS

DATE

M   T   W   Th   F   Sa   Su

▷ _____

▷ _____

▷ _____

TODAY'S TOP 3

To Do

- ☐ _____
- ☐ _____
- ☐ _____
- ☐ _____
- ☐ _____
- ☐ _____
- ☐ _____
- ☐ _____
- ☐ _____
- ☐ _____

Income Generating Activities

APPOINTMENTS

6am _____

7am _____

8am _____

9am _____

10am _____

11am _____

12pm _____

1pm _____

2pm _____

3pm _____

4pm _____

5pm _____

6pm _____

7pm _____

▷ AFFIRMATIONS

▷ SALES GOALS

▷ NOTES / IDEAS

DATE

M T W Th F Sa Su

TODAY'S TOP 3

▷
▷
▷

To Do

- ☐
- ☐
- ☐
- ☐
- ☐
- ☐
- ☐
- ☐
- ☐
- ☐

Income Generating Activities

APPOINTMENTS

6am
7am
8am
9am
10am
11am
12pm
1pm
2pm
3pm
4pm
5pm
6pm
7pm

▷ AFFIRMATIONS

▷ SALES GOALS

▷ NOTES / IDEAS

THIS WEEK IN REVIEW

This Week's Big Wins

☐ _____

☐ _____

☐ _____

☐ _____

☐ _____

☐ _____

☐ _____

☐ _____

NOTES

_____

_____

_____

_____

_____

_____

MON

NEXT WEEK AT A GLANCE

TUE

WED

THU

FRI

SAT

SUN

DATE

M   T   W   Th   F   Sa   Su

▷ _____

▷ _____

▷ _____

TODAY'S TOP 3

To Do

☐ _____

☐ _____

☐ _____

☐ _____

☐ _____

☐ _____

☐ _____

☐ _____

☐ _____

☐ _____

Income Generating Activities

APPOINTMENTS

6am

7am

8am

9am

10am

11am

12pm

1pm

2pm

3pm

4pm

5pm

6pm

7pm

▷ AFFIRMATIONS

▷ SALES GOALS

▷ NOTES / IDEAS

DATE

M   T   W   Th   F   Sa   Su

▷ _____

▷ _____

▷ _____

To Do

- ☐ _____
- ☐ _____
- ☐ _____
- ☐ _____
- ☐ _____
- ☐ _____
- ☐ _____
- ☐ _____
- ☐ _____
- ☐ _____

Income Generating Activities

_____

_____

_____

_____

_____

_____

_____

_____

_____

_____

APPOINTMENTS

6am _____

7am _____

8am _____

9am _____

10am _____

11am _____

12pm _____

1pm _____

2pm _____

3pm _____

4pm _____

5pm _____

6pm _____

7pm _____

▷ AFFIRMATIONS

▷ SALES GOALS

▷ NOTES / IDEAS

DATE

M   T   W   Th   F   Sa   Su

▷ _____

▷ _____

▷ _____

To Do

- ☐ _____
- ☐ _____
- ☐ _____
- ☐ _____
- ☐ _____
- ☐ _____
- ☐ _____
- ☐ _____
- ☐ _____
- ☐ _____
- ☐ _____

Income Generating Activities

APPOINTMENTS

6am	
7am	
8am	
9am	
10am	
11am	
12pm	
1pm	
2pm	
3pm	
4pm	
5pm	
6pm	
7pm	

▷ AFFIRMATIONS

▷ SALES GOALS

▷ NOTES / IDEAS

DATE

M T W Th F Sa Su

To Do

- [ ]
- [ ]
- [ ]
- [ ]
- [ ]
- [ ]
- [ ]
- [ ]
- [ ]
- [ ]

Income Generating Activities

APPOINTMENTS

6am
7am
8am
9am
10am
11am
12pm
1pm
2pm
3pm
4pm
5pm
6pm
7pm

AFFIRMATIONS

SALES GOALS

NOTES / IDEAS

DATE

M T W Th F Sa Su

TODAY'S TOP 3

▷
▷
▷

To Do

☐
☐
☐
☐
☐
☐
☐
☐
☐
☐

Income Generating Activities

APPOINTMENTS

6am
7am
8am
9am
10am
11am
12pm
1pm
2pm
3pm
4pm
5pm
6pm
7pm

▷ AFFIRMATIONS

▷ SALES GOALS

▷ NOTES / IDEAS

DATE

M T W Th F Sa Su

>
>
>

TODAY'S TOP 3

To Do

- [ ]
- [ ]
- [ ]
- [ ]
- [ ]
- [ ]
- [ ]
- [ ]
- [ ]
- [ ]

Income Generating Activities

APPOINTMENTS

6am
7am
8am
9am
10am
11am
12pm
1pm
2pm
3pm
4pm
5pm
6pm
7pm

> AFFIRMATIONS

> SALES GOALS

> NOTES / IDEAS

DATE

M   T   W   Th   F   Sa   Su

⊳

⊳

⊳

To Do

- ☐
- ☐
- ☐
- ☐
- ☐
- ☐
- ☐
- ☐
- ☐
- ☐
- ☐

Income Generating Activities

APPOINTMENTS

6am

7am   ⊳ AFFIRMATIONS

8am

9am

10am

11am   ⊳ SALES GOALS

12pm

1pm

2pm

3pm

4pm   ⊳ NOTES / IDEAS

5pm

6pm

7pm

THIS WEEK IN REVIEW

This Week's Big Wins

☐ _____

☐ _____

☐ _____

☐ _____

☐ _____

☐ _____

☐ _____

☐ _____

NOTES

_____

_____

_____

_____

_____

_____

_____

NEXT WEEK AT A GLANCE

MON _____

TUE _____

WED _____

THU _____

FRI _____

SAT _____

SUN _____

DATE

M   T   W   Th   F   Sa   Su

▷ _____

▷ _____

▷ _____

TODAY'S TOP 3

To Do

☐ _____

☐ _____

☐ _____

☐ _____

☐ _____

☐ _____

☐ _____

☐ _____

☐ _____

☐ _____

☐ _____

Income Generating Activities

APPOINTMENTS

6am

7am

8am

9am

10am

11am

12pm

1pm

2pm

3pm

4pm

5pm

6pm

7pm

▷ AFFIRMATIONS

▷ SALES GOALS

▷ NOTES / IDEAS

DATE

M   T   W   Th   F   Sa   Su

TODAY'S TOP 3

▷ _____

▷ _____

▷ _____

To Do

- ☐ _____
- ☐ _____
- ☐ _____
- ☐ _____
- ☐ _____
- ☐ _____
- ☐ _____
- ☐ _____
- ☐ _____
- ☐ _____

Income Generating Activities

APPOINTMENTS

6am

7am

8am

9am

10am

11am

12pm

1pm

2pm

3pm

4pm

5pm

6pm

7pm

▷ AFFIRMATIONS

▷ SALES GOALS

▷ NOTES / IDEAS

DATE

M   T   W   Th   F   Sa   Su

TODAY'S TOP 3

> _____
> _____
> _____

To Do

- [ ] _____
- [ ] _____
- [ ] _____
- [ ] _____
- [ ] _____
- [ ] _____
- [ ] _____
- [ ] _____
- [ ] _____
- [ ] _____
- [ ] _____

Income Generating Activities

APPOINTMENTS

6am

7am

8am

9am

10am

11am

12pm

1pm

2pm

3pm

4pm

5pm

6pm

7pm

> AFFIRMATIONS

> SALES GOALS

> NOTES / IDEAS

DATE

M   T   W   Th   F   Sa   Su

TODAY'S TOP 3

To Do

- ☐
- ☐
- ☐
- ☐
- ☐
- ☐
- ☐
- ☐
- ☐
- ☐

Income Generating Activities

APPOINTMENTS

6am

7am

8am

9am

10am

11am

12pm

1pm

2pm

3pm

4pm

5pm

6pm

7pm

AFFIRMATIONS

SALES GOALS

NOTES / IDEAS

DATE

M　T　W　Th　F　Sa　Su

To Do

- [ ]
- [ ]
- [ ]
- [ ]
- [ ]
- [ ]
- [ ]
- [ ]
- [ ]
- [ ]
- [ ]

Income Generating Activities

APPOINTMENTS

6am
7am
8am
9am
10am
11am
12pm
1pm
2pm
3pm
4pm
5pm
6pm
7pm

AFFIRMATIONS

SALES GOALS

NOTES / IDEAS

DATE

M T W Th F Sa Su

TODAY'S TOP 3

▷ _____

▷ _____

▷ _____

To Do

☐ _____

☐ _____

☐ _____

☐ _____

☐ _____

☐ _____

☐ _____

☐ _____

☐ _____

☐ _____

Income Generating Activities

APPOINTMENTS

6am

7am

8am

9am

10am

11am

12pm

1pm

2pm

3pm

4pm

5pm

6pm

7pm

▷ AFFIRMATIONS

▷ SALES GOALS

▷ NOTES / IDEAS

DATE

M	T	W	Th	F	Sa	Su

▷ ....

▷ ....

▷ ....

To Do

- ☐ ....
- ☐ ....
- ☐ ....
- ☐ ....
- ☐ ....
- ☐ ....
- ☐ ....
- ☐ ....
- ☐ ....
- ☐ ....
- ☐ ....

Income Generating Activities

APPOINTMENTS

6am	
7am	
8am	
9am	
10am	
11am	
12pm	
1pm	
2pm	
3pm	
4pm	
5pm	
6pm	
7pm	

▷ AFFIRMATIONS

▷ SALES GOALS

▷ NOTES / IDEAS

THIS WEEK IN REVIEW

This Week's Big Wins

- [ ]
- [ ]
- [ ]
- [ ]
- [ ]
- [ ]
- [ ]

NOTES

NEXT WEEK AT A GLANCE

MON

TUE

WED

THU

FRI

SAT

SUN

_____ MONTH IN REVIEW

MONTHLY WINS

≫	≫
≫	≫
≫	≫
≫	≫

INCOME GENERATING HABITS THAT SUPPORT MONTHLY GOALS

≫	☐ DAILY HABIT	☐ WEEKLY HABIT
≫	☐ DAILY HABIT	☐ WEEKLY HABIT
≫	☐ DAILY HABIT	☐ WEEKLY HABIT
≫	☐ DAILY HABIT	☐ WEEKLY HABIT
≫	☐ DAILY HABIT	☐ WEEKLY HABIT

DAILY SALES

1.	11.	21.
2.	12.	22.
3.	13.	23.
4.	14.	24.
5.	15.	25.
6.	16.	26.
7.	17.	27.
8.	18.	28.
9.	19.	29.
10.	20.	30.

≫ *The best way to get something done is to begin.*

Make It Happen

MONTH _____

SUNDAY	MONDAY	TUESDAY	WEDNESDAY

Action is the foundational key to all success. – *Pablo Picasso*

THURSDAY	FRIDAY	SATURDAY

NOTES

_____

_____

_____

_____

_____

_____

_____

_____

_____

_____

_____

_____

_____

_____

_____

_____

_____

_____

_____

_____

_____

_____

_____

_____

DATE			M	T	W	Th	F	Sa	Su

▷ _____

▷ _____

▷ _____

To Do

☐ _____

☐ _____

☐ _____

☐ _____

☐ _____

☐ _____

☐ _____

☐ _____

☐ _____

☐ _____

☐ _____

Income Generating Activities

_____

_____

_____

_____

_____

_____

_____

_____

_____

APPOINTMENTS

6am _____

7am _____

8am _____

9am _____

10am _____

11am _____

12pm _____

1pm _____

2pm _____

3pm _____

4pm _____

5pm _____

6pm _____

7pm _____

▷ AFFIRMATIONS

▷ SALES GOALS

▷ NOTES / IDEAS

DATE

M   T   W   Th   F   Sa   Su

▷ _____

▷ _____

▷ _____

TODAY'S TOP 3

To Do

☐ _____
☐ _____
☐ _____
☐ _____
☐ _____
☐ _____
☐ _____
☐ _____
☐ _____
☐ _____

Income Generating Activities

_____
_____
_____
_____
_____
_____
_____
_____
_____
_____

APPOINTMENTS

6am _____
7am _____
8am _____
9am _____
10am _____
11am _____
12pm _____
1pm _____
2pm _____
3pm _____
4pm _____
5pm _____
6pm _____
7pm _____

▷ AFFIRMATIONS

▷ SALES GOALS

▷ NOTES / IDEAS

DATE

M   T   W   Th   F   Sa   Su

▷

▷

▷

TODAY'S TOP 3

To Do

☐

☐

☐

☐

☐

☐

☐

☐

☐

☐

Income Generating Activities

APPOINTMENTS

6am

7am

8am

9am

10am

11am

12pm

1pm

2pm

3pm

4pm

5pm

6pm

7pm

▷ AFFIRMATIONS

▷ SALES GOALS

▷ NOTES / IDEAS

DATE

M   T   W   Th   F   Sa   Su

▷ _____

▷ _____

▷ _____

To Do

- ☐
- ☐
- ☐
- ☐
- ☐
- ☐
- ☐
- ☐
- ☐
- ☐

Income Generating Activities

APPOINTMENTS

6am
7am
8am
9am
10am
11am
12pm
1pm
2pm
3pm
4pm
5pm
6pm
7pm

▷ AFFIRMATIONS

▷ SALES GOALS

▷ NOTES / IDEAS

DATE			M	T	W	Th	F	Sa	Su

TODAY'S TOP 3

To Do

- ☐
- ☐
- ☐
- ☐
- ☐
- ☐
- ☐
- ☐
- ☐
- ☐

Income Generating Activities

APPOINTMENTS

6am	
7am	
8am	
9am	
10am	
11am	
12pm	
1pm	
2pm	
3pm	
4pm	
5pm	
6pm	
7pm	

AFFIRMATIONS

SALES GOALS

NOTES / IDEAS

DATE

M T W Th F Sa Su

▷ _____

▷ _____

▷ _____

To Do

☐ _____

☐ _____

☐ _____

☐ _____

☐ _____

☐ _____

☐ _____

☐ _____

☐ _____

☐ _____

Income Generating Activities

_____

_____

_____

_____

_____

_____

_____

_____

_____

APPOINTMENTS

6am _____

7am _____

8am _____

9am _____

10am _____

11am _____

12pm _____

1pm _____

2pm _____

3pm _____

4pm _____

5pm _____

6pm _____

7pm _____

▷ AFFIRMATIONS

▷ SALES GOALS

▷ NOTES / IDEAS

DATE

M   T   W   Th   F   Sa   Su

▷

▷

▷

TODAY'S TOP 3

To Do

- ☐
- ☐
- ☐
- ☐
- ☐
- ☐
- ☐
- ☐
- ☐
- ☐
- ☐

Income Generating Activities

APPOINTMENTS

6am

7am

8am

9am

10am

11am

12pm

1pm

2pm

3pm

4pm

5pm

6pm

7pm

▷ AFFIRMATIONS

▷ SALES GOALS

▷ NOTES / IDEAS

THIS WEEK IN REVIEW

This Week's Big Wins

- [ ]
- [ ]
- [ ]
- [ ]
- [ ]
- [ ]
- [ ]
- [ ]

NOTES

NEXT WEEK AT A GLANCE

MON

TUE

WED

THU

FRI

SAT

SUN

DATE		M T W Th F Sa Su

To Do

- [ ]
- [ ]
- [ ]
- [ ]
- [ ]
- [ ]
- [ ]
- [ ]
- [ ]
- [ ]
- [ ]

Income Generating Activities

APPOINTMENTS

6am
7am
8am
9am
10am
11am
12pm
1pm
2pm
3pm
4pm
5pm
6pm
7pm

AFFIRMATIONS

SALES GOALS

NOTES / IDEAS

M   T   W   Th   F   Sa   Su

TODAY'S TOP 3

▷
▷
▷

To Do

☐
☐
☐
☐
☐
☐
☐
☐
☐
☐
☐

Income Generating Activities

APPOINTMENTS

6am
7am
8am
9am
10am
11am
12pm
1pm
2pm
3pm
4pm
5pm
6pm
7pm

▷ AFFIRMATIONS

▷ SALES GOALS

▷ NOTES / IDEAS

DATE		M	T	W	Th	F	Sa	Su

▷ _____

▷ _____

▷ _____

To Do

☐ _____

☐ _____

☐ _____

☐ _____

☐ _____

☐ _____

☐ _____

☐ _____

☐ _____

☐ _____

☐ _____

Income Generating Activities

APPOINTMENTS

6am

7am

8am

9am

10am

11am

12pm

1pm

2pm

3pm

4pm

5pm

6pm

7pm

▷ AFFIRMATIONS

▷ SALES GOALS

▷ NOTES / IDEAS

DATE			M	T	W	Th	F	Sa	Su

▷ _____

▷ _____

▷ _____

TODAY'S TOP 3

To Do

☐ _____

☐ _____

☐ _____

☐ _____

☐ _____

☐ _____

☐ _____

☐ _____

☐ _____

☐ _____

Income Generating Activities

APPOINTMENTS

6am _____

7am _____

8am _____

9am _____

10am _____

11am _____

12pm _____

1pm _____

2pm _____

3pm _____

4pm _____

5pm _____

6pm _____

7pm _____

▷ AFFIRMATIONS

▷ SALES GOALS

▷ NOTES / IDEAS

▷ _____

▷ _____

▷ _____

TODAY'S TOP 3

To Do

- ☐ _____
- ☐ _____
- ☐ _____
- ☐ _____
- ☐ _____
- ☐ _____
- ☐ _____
- ☐ _____
- ☐ _____
- ☐ _____
- ☐ _____

Income Generating Activities

_____

_____

_____

_____

_____

_____

_____

_____

_____

APPOINTMENTS

6am	
7am	
8am	
9am	
10am	
11am	
12pm	
1pm	
2pm	
3pm	
4pm	
5pm	
6pm	
7pm	

▷ AFFIRMATIONS

▷ SALES GOALS

▷ NOTES / IDEAS

DATE

M T W Th F Sa Su

▷ _____

▷ _____

▷ _____

TODAY'S TOP 3

To Do

- ☐ _____
- ☐ _____
- ☐ _____
- ☐ _____
- ☐ _____
- ☐ _____
- ☐ _____
- ☐ _____
- ☐ _____
- ☐ _____
- ☐ _____

Income Generating Activities

_____

_____

_____

_____

_____

_____

_____

_____

_____

_____

_____

APPOINTMENTS

6am _____

7am _____

8am _____

9am _____

10am _____

11am _____

12pm _____

1pm _____

2pm _____

3pm _____

4pm _____

5pm _____

6pm _____

7pm _____

▷ AFFIRMATIONS

▷ SALES GOALS

▷ NOTES / IDEAS

DATE

| M | T | W | Th | F | Sa | Su |

TODAY'S TOP 3

▷ _____

▷ _____

▷ _____

To Do

☐ _____

☐ _____

☐ _____

☐ _____

☐ _____

☐ _____

☐ _____

☐ _____

☐ _____

☐ _____

Income Generating Activities

APPOINTMENTS

6am	
7am	
8am	
9am	
10am	
11am	
12pm	
1pm	
2pm	
3pm	
4pm	
5pm	
6pm	
7pm	

▷ AFFIRMATIONS

▷ SALES GOALS

▷ NOTES / IDEAS

THIS WEEK IN REVIEW

This Week's Big Wins

- [ ]
- [ ]
- [ ]
- [ ]
- [ ]
- [ ]
- [ ]
- [ ]

NOTES

NEXT WEEK AT A GLANCE

MON

TUE

WED

THU

FRI

SAT

SUN

DATE

M   T   W   Th   F   Sa   Su

▷
▷
▷

TODAY'S TOP 3

To Do

- [ ]
- [ ]
- [ ]
- [ ]
- [ ]
- [ ]
- [ ]
- [ ]
- [ ]
- [ ]
- [ ]

Income Generating Activities

APPOINTMENTS

| 6am |
| 7am |
| 8am |
| 9am |
| 10am |
| 11am |
| 12pm |
| 1pm |
| 2pm |
| 3pm |
| 4pm |
| 5pm |
| 6pm |
| 7pm |

▷ AFFIRMATIONS

▷ SALES GOALS

▷ NOTES / IDEAS

DATE

M   T   W   Th   F   Sa   Su

▷ _____

▷ _____

▷ _____

TODAY'S TOP 3

To Do

☐ _____
☐ _____
☐ _____
☐ _____
☐ _____
☐ _____
☐ _____
☐ _____
☐ _____
☐ _____

Income Generating Activities

APPOINTMENTS

6am
7am
8am
9am
10am
11am
12pm
1pm
2pm
3pm
4pm
5pm
6pm
7pm

▷ AFFIRMATIONS

▷ SALES GOALS

▷ NOTES / IDEAS

DATE

M   T   W   Th   F   Sa   Su

▷ _____

▷ _____

▷ _____

TODAY'S TOP 3

To Do

☐ _____
☐ _____
☐ _____
☐ _____
☐ _____
☐ _____
☐ _____
☐ _____
☐ _____
☐ _____
☐ _____

Income Generating Activities

APPOINTMENTS

6am	
7am	
8am	
9am	
10am	
11am	
12pm	
1pm	
2pm	
3pm	
4pm	
5pm	
6pm	
7pm	

▷ AFFIRMATIONS

▷ SALES GOALS

▷ NOTES / IDEAS

DATE

M   T   W   Th   F   Sa   Su

▷ _____

▷ _____

▷ _____

TODAY'S TOP 3

To Do

☐ _____

☐ _____

☐ _____

☐ _____

☐ _____

☐ _____

☐ _____

☐ _____

☐ _____

☐ _____

Income Generating Activities

_____

_____

_____

_____

_____

_____

_____

_____

_____

_____

APPOINTMENTS

6am _____

7am _____

8am _____

9am _____

10am _____

11am _____

12pm _____

1pm _____

2pm _____

3pm _____

4pm _____

5pm _____

6pm _____

7pm _____

▷ AFFIRMATIONS

▷ SALES GOALS

▷ NOTES / IDEAS

DATE

M   T   W   Th   F   Sa   Su

▷

▷

▷

To Do	Income Generating Activities
☐	
☐	
☐	
☐	
☐	
☐	
☐	
☐	
☐	
☐	

APPOINTMENTS

6am

7am

8am

9am

10am

11am

12pm

1pm

2pm

3pm

4pm

5pm

6pm

7pm

▷ AFFIRMATIONS

▷ SALES GOALS

▷ NOTES / IDEAS

DATE

M T W Th F Sa Su

▷ _____

▷ _____

▷ _____

TODAY'S TOP 3

To Do

☐ _____
☐ _____
☐ _____
☐ _____
☐ _____
☐ _____
☐ _____
☐ _____
☐ _____
☐ _____

Income Generating Activities

APPOINTMENTS

6am _____
7am _____
8am _____
9am _____
10am _____
11am _____
12pm _____
1pm _____
2pm _____
3pm _____
4pm _____
5pm _____
6pm _____
7pm _____

▷ AFFIRMATIONS

▷ SALES GOALS

▷ NOTES / IDEAS

DATE

M   T   W   Th   F   Sa   Su

▷ _____

▷ _____

▷ _____

To Do

☐ _____

☐ _____

☐ _____

☐ _____

☐ _____

☐ _____

☐ _____

☐ _____

☐ _____

☐ _____

☐ _____

Income Generating Activities

APPOINTMENTS

6am _____

7am _____

8am _____

9am _____

10am _____

11am _____

12pm _____

1pm _____

2pm _____

3pm _____

4pm _____

5pm _____

6pm _____

7pm _____

▷ AFFIRMATIONS

▷ SALES GOALS

▷ NOTES / IDEAS

THIS WEEK IN REVIEW

This Week's Big Wins

- [ ]
- [ ]
- [ ]
- [ ]
- [ ]
- [ ]
- [ ]
- [ ]

NOTES

NEXT WEEK AT A GLANCE

MON

TUE

WED

THU

FRI

SAT

SUN

DATE				M	T	W	Th	F	Sa	Su

▷ _____

▷ _____

▷ _____

TODAY'S TOP 3

To Do

☐ _____

☐ _____

☐ _____

☐ _____

☐ _____

☐ _____

☐ _____

☐ _____

☐ _____

☐ _____

☐ _____

Income Generating Activities

APPOINTMENTS

6am	
7am	
8am	
9am	
10am	
11am	
12pm	
1pm	
2pm	
3pm	
4pm	
5pm	
6pm	
7pm	

▷ AFFIRMATIONS

▷ SALES GOALS

▷ NOTES / IDEAS

DATE

M   T   W   Th   F   Sa   Su

▷ _____

▷ _____

▷ _____

TODAY'S TOP 3

To Do

☐ _____
☐ _____
☐ _____
☐ _____
☐ _____
☐ _____
☐ _____
☐ _____
☐ _____
☐ _____
☐ _____

Income Generating Activities

APPOINTMENTS

6am
7am
8am
9am
10am
11am
12pm
1pm
2pm
3pm
4pm
5pm
6pm
7pm

▷ AFFIRMATIONS

▷ SALES GOALS

▷ NOTES / IDEAS

DATE

M   T   W   Th   F   Sa   Su

▷ _____

▷ _____

▷ _____

TODAY'S TOP 3

To Do

☐ _____
☐ _____
☐ _____
☐ _____
☐ _____
☐ _____
☐ _____
☐ _____
☐ _____
☐ _____
☐ _____

Income Generating Activities

APPOINTMENTS

6am _____
7am _____
8am _____
9am _____
10am _____
11am _____
12pm _____
1pm _____
2pm _____
3pm _____
4pm _____
5pm _____
6pm _____
7pm _____

▷ AFFIRMATIONS

▷ SALES GOALS

▷ NOTES / IDEAS

DATE		M	T	W	Th	F	Sa	Su

▷ _____

▷ _____

▷ _____

To Do

- ☐ _____
- ☐ _____
- ☐ _____
- ☐ _____
- ☐ _____
- ☐ _____
- ☐ _____
- ☐ _____
- ☐ _____
- ☐ _____
- ☐ _____

Income Generating Activities

APPOINTMENTS

6am

7am

8am

9am

10am

11am

12pm

1pm

2pm

3pm

4pm

5pm

6pm

7pm

▷ AFFIRMATIONS

▷ SALES GOALS

▷ NOTES / IDEAS

▷ _____

▷ _____

▷ _____

TODAY'S TOP 3

To Do

☐ _____

☐ _____

☐ _____

☐ _____

☐ _____

☐ _____

☐ _____

☐ _____

☐ _____

☐ _____

☐ _____

Income Generating Activities

APPOINTMENTS

6am _____

7am _____

8am _____

9am _____

10am _____

11am _____

12pm _____

1pm _____

2pm _____

3pm _____

4pm _____

5pm _____

6pm _____

7pm _____

▷ **AFFIRMATIONS**

▷ **SALES GOALS**

▷ **NOTES / IDEAS**

DATE

M T W Th F Sa Su

▷
▷
▷

To Do

- ☐
- ☐
- ☐
- ☐
- ☐
- ☐
- ☐
- ☐
- ☐
- ☐

Income Generating Activities

APPOINTMENTS

6am
7am
8am
9am
10am
11am
12pm
1pm
2pm
3pm
4pm
5pm
6pm
7pm

▷ AFFIRMATIONS

▷ SALES GOALS

▷ NOTES / IDEAS

DATE

M   T   W   Th   F   Sa   Su

▷ _____

▷ _____

▷ _____

TODAY'S TOP 3

To Do

- ☐ _____
- ☐ _____
- ☐ _____
- ☐ _____
- ☐ _____
- ☐ _____
- ☐ _____
- ☐ _____
- ☐ _____
- ☐ _____
- ☐ _____

Income Generating Activities

_____

_____

_____

_____

_____

_____

_____

_____

_____

_____

_____

APPOINTMENTS

6am

7am

8am

9am

10am

11am

12pm

1pm

2pm

3pm

4pm

5pm

6pm

7pm

▷ AFFIRMATIONS

▷ SALES GOALS

▷ NOTES / IDEAS

THIS WEEK IN REVIEW

This Week's Big Wins

- [ ]
- [ ]
- [ ]
- [ ]
- [ ]
- [ ]
- [ ]
- [ ]

NOTES

NEXT WEEK AT A GLANCE

MON

TUE

WED

THU

FRI

SAT

SUN

DATE

M　T　W　Th　F　Sa　Su

▷ _____

▷ _____

▷ _____

TODAY'S TOP 3

To Do

☐ _____

☐ _____

☐ _____

☐ _____

☐ _____

☐ _____

☐ _____

☐ _____

☐ _____

☐ _____

Income Generating Activities

_____

_____

_____

_____

_____

_____

_____

_____

_____

APPOINTMENTS

6am

7am

8am

9am

10am

11am

12pm

1pm

2pm

3pm

4pm

5pm

6pm

7pm

▷ AFFIRMATIONS

▷ SALES GOALS

▷ NOTES / IDEAS

DATE

M   T   W   Th   F   Sa   Su

▷ _____

▷ _____

▷ _____

To Do

- ☐ _____
- ☐ _____
- ☐ _____
- ☐ _____
- ☐ _____
- ☐ _____
- ☐ _____
- ☐ _____
- ☐ _____
- ☐ _____

Income Generating Activities

APPOINTMENTS

6am

7am

8am

9am

10am

11am

12pm

1pm

2pm

3pm

4pm

5pm

6pm

7pm

▷ AFFIRMATIONS

▷ SALES GOALS

▷ NOTES / IDEAS

DATE

M   T   W   Th   F   Sa   Su

▷

▷

▷

To Do

- ☐
- ☐
- ☐
- ☐
- ☐
- ☐
- ☐
- ☐
- ☐
- ☐
- ☐

Income Generating Activities

APPOINTMENTS

6am	
7am	
8am	
9am	
10am	
11am	
12pm	
1pm	
2pm	
3pm	
4pm	
5pm	
6pm	
7pm	

▷ AFFIRMATIONS

▷ SALES GOALS

▷ NOTES / IDEAS

DATE

M T W Th F Sa Su

▷
▷
▷

TODAY'S TOP 3

To Do

☐
☐
☐
☐
☐
☐
☐
☐
☐
☐

Income Generating Activities

APPOINTMENTS

6am
7am
8am
9am
10am
11am
12pm
1pm
2pm
3pm
4pm
5pm
6pm
7pm

▷ AFFIRMATIONS

▷ SALES GOALS

▷ NOTES / IDEAS

DATE

M   T   W   Th   F   Sa   Su

▷ _____

▷ _____

▷ _____

To Do

☐ _____

☐ _____

☐ _____

☐ _____

☐ _____

☐ _____

☐ _____

☐ _____

☐ _____

☐ _____

☐ _____

Income Generating Activities

APPOINTMENTS

6am _____

7am _____

8am _____

9am _____

10am _____

11am _____

12pm _____

1pm _____

2pm _____

3pm _____

4pm _____

5pm _____

6pm _____

7pm _____

▷ AFFIRMATIONS

▷ SALES GOALS

▷ NOTES / IDEAS

DATE

M   T   W   Th   F   Sa   Su

TODAY'S TOP 3

▷

▷

▷

To Do

- ☐
- ☐
- ☐
- ☐
- ☐
- ☐
- ☐
- ☐
- ☐
- ☐

Income Generating Activities

APPOINTMENTS

6am

7am

8am

9am

10am

11am

12pm

1pm

2pm

3pm

4pm

5pm

6pm

7pm

▷ AFFIRMATIONS

▷ SALES GOALS

▷ NOTES / IDEAS

DATE

M   T   W   Th   F   Sa   Su

▷
▷
▷

To Do

- ☐
- ☐
- ☐
- ☐
- ☐
- ☐
- ☐
- ☐
- ☐
- ☐
- ☐

Income Generating Activities

APPOINTMENTS

| 6am |
| 7am |
| 8am |
| 9am |
| 10am |
| 11am |
| 12pm |
| 1pm |
| 2pm |
| 3pm |
| 4pm |
| 5pm |
| 6pm |
| 7pm |

▷ AFFIRMATIONS

▷ SALES GOALS

▷ NOTES / IDEAS

THIS WEEK IN REVIEW

This Week's Big Wins

- ☐
- ☐
- ☐
- ☐
- ☐
- ☐
- ☐
- ☐

NOTES

NEXT WEEK AT A GLANCE
MON
TUE
WED
THU
FRI
SAT
SUN

_____ MONTH IN REVIEW

MONTHLY WINS

▷
▷

▷
▷

▷
▷

▷
▷

INCOME GENERATING HABITS THAT SUPPORT MONTHLY GOALS

▷   ☐ DAILY HABIT   ☐ WEEKLY HABIT

▷   ☐ DAILY HABIT   ☐ WEEKLY HABIT

▷   ☐ DAILY HABIT   ☐ WEEKLY HABIT

▷   ☐ DAILY HABIT   ☐ WEEKLY HABIT

▷   ☐ DAILY HABIT   ☐ WEEKLY HABIT

DAILY SALES

1.	11.	21.
2.	12.	22.
3.	13.	23.
4.	14.	24.
5.	15.	25.
6.	16.	26.
7.	17.	27.
8.	18.	28.
9.	19.	29.
10.	20.	30.

▷ _The secret of your success is found in your daily routine._

You Were Made For This.

MONTH _____

SUNDAY	MONDAY	TUESDAY	WEDNESDAY

A winner is a dreamer who never gives up. – *Nelson Mandella*

THURSDAY	FRIDAY	SATURDAY	NOTES

DATE

M T W Th F Sa Su

▷
▷
▷

To Do

- ☐
- ☐
- ☐
- ☐
- ☐
- ☐
- ☐
- ☐
- ☐
- ☐
- ☐

Income Generating Activities

APPOINTMENTS

6am
7am
8am
9am
10am
11am
12pm
1pm
2pm
3pm
4pm
5pm
6pm
7pm

▷ AFFIRMATIONS

▷ SALES GOALS

▷ NOTES / IDEAS

DATE

M   T   W   Th   F   Sa   Su

▷ _____

▷ _____

▷ _____

TODAY'S TOP 3

To Do

- ☐ _____
- ☐ _____
- ☐ _____
- ☐ _____
- ☐ _____
- ☐ _____
- ☐ _____
- ☐ _____
- ☐ _____
- ☐ _____

Income Generating Activities

_____

_____

_____

_____

_____

_____

_____

_____

_____

_____

APPOINTMENTS

6am _____

7am _____

8am _____

9am _____

10am _____

11am _____

12pm _____

1pm _____

2pm _____

3pm _____

4pm _____

5pm _____

6pm _____

7pm _____

▷ **AFFIRMATIONS**

▷ **SALES GOALS**

▷ **NOTES / IDEAS**

DATE

M T W Th F Sa Su

▷ _____

▷ _____

▷ _____

TODAY'S TOP 3

To Do

☐ _____

☐ _____

☐ _____

☐ _____

☐ _____

☐ _____

☐ _____

☐ _____

☐ _____

☐ _____

☐ _____

Income Generating Activities

_____

_____

_____

_____

_____

_____

_____

_____

_____

_____

APPOINTMENTS

6am _____

7am _____

8am _____

9am _____

10am _____

11am _____

12pm _____

1pm _____

2pm _____

3pm _____

4pm _____

5pm _____

6pm _____

7pm _____

▷ AFFIRMATIONS

▷ SALES GOALS

▷ NOTES / IDEAS

DATE

M T W Th F Sa Su

TODAY'S TOP 3

▷ ....

▷ ....

▷ ....

To Do

- ☐
- ☐
- ☐
- ☐
- ☐
- ☐
- ☐
- ☐
- ☐
- ☐

Income Generating Activities

APPOINTMENTS

6am

7am

8am

9am

10am

11am

12pm

1pm

2pm

3pm

4pm

5pm

6pm

7pm

▷ AFFIRMATIONS

▷ SALES GOALS

▷ NOTES / IDEAS

DATE

M   T   W   Th   F   Sa   Su

TODAY'S TOP 3

To Do

- [ ]
- [ ]
- [ ]
- [ ]
- [ ]
- [ ]
- [ ]
- [ ]
- [ ]
- [ ]
- [ ]

Income Generating Activities

APPOINTMENTS

6am	
7am	
8am	
9am	
10am	
11am	
12pm	
1pm	
2pm	
3pm	
4pm	
5pm	
6pm	
7pm	

AFFIRMATIONS

SALES GOALS

NOTES / IDEAS

DATE

M   T   W   Th   F   Sa   Su

TODAY'S TOP 3

To Do

- [ ]
- [ ]
- [ ]
- [ ]
- [ ]
- [ ]
- [ ]
- [ ]
- [ ]
- [ ]

Income Generating Activities

APPOINTMENTS

6am
7am
8am
9am
10am
11am
12pm
1pm
2pm
3pm
4pm
5pm
6pm
7pm

AFFIRMATIONS

SALES GOALS

NOTES / IDEAS

DATE

M   T   W   Th   F   Sa   Su

▷ _____

▷ _____

▷ _____

TODAY'S TOP 3

To Do

- ☐ _____
- ☐ _____
- ☐ _____
- ☐ _____
- ☐ _____
- ☐ _____
- ☐ _____
- ☐ _____
- ☐ _____
- ☐ _____
- ☐ _____

Income Generating Activities

APPOINTMENTS

6am	
7am	
8am	
9am	
10am	
11am	
12pm	
1pm	
2pm	
3pm	
4pm	
5pm	
6pm	
7pm	

▷ AFFIRMATIONS

▷ SALES GOALS

▷ NOTES / IDEAS

THIS WEEK IN REVIEW

This Week's Big Wins

- [ ]
- [ ]
- [ ]
- [ ]
- [ ]
- [ ]
- [ ]
- [ ]

NOTES

NEXT WEEK AT A GLANCE

MON

TUE

WED

THU

FRI

SAT

SUN

DATE

M   T   W   Th   F   Sa   Su

▷ _____
▷ _____
▷ _____

TODAY'S TOP 3

To Do

☐ _____
☐ _____
☐ _____
☐ _____
☐ _____
☐ _____
☐ _____
☐ _____
☐ _____
☐ _____
☐ _____

Income Generating Activities

_____
_____
_____
_____
_____
_____
_____
_____
_____

APPOINTMENTS

6am _____

7am _____

8am _____

9am _____

10am _____

11am _____

12pm _____

1pm _____

2pm _____

3pm _____

4pm _____

5pm _____

6pm _____

7pm _____

▷ AFFIRMATIONS

▷ SALES GOALS

▷ NOTES / IDEAS

DATE

M T W Th F Sa Su

➤ _____

➤ _____

➤ _____

TODAY'S TOP 3

To Do

☐ _____
☐ _____
☐ _____
☐ _____
☐ _____
☐ _____
☐ _____
☐ _____
☐ _____
☐ _____

Income Generating Activities

APPOINTMENTS

6am _____
7am _____
8am _____
9am _____
10am _____
11am _____
12pm _____
1pm _____
2pm _____
3pm _____
4pm _____
5pm _____
6pm _____
7pm _____

➤ AFFIRMATIONS

➤ SALES GOALS

➤ NOTES / IDEAS

▷ _____

▷ _____

▷ _____

TODAY'S TOP 3

To Do

☐ _____

☐ _____

☐ _____

☐ _____

☐ _____

☐ _____

☐ _____

☐ _____

☐ _____

☐ _____

☐ _____

Income Generating Activities

APPOINTMENTS

6am

7am

8am

9am

10am

11am

12pm

1pm

2pm

3pm

4pm

5pm

6pm

7pm

▷ AFFIRMATIONS

▷ SALES GOALS

▷ NOTES / IDEAS

DATE

M T W Th F Sa Su

TODAY'S TOP 3

▷
▷
▷

To Do

☐
☐
☐
☐
☐
☐
☐
☐
☐
☐

Income Generating Activities

APPOINTMENTS

6am
7am
8am
9am
10am
11am
12pm
1pm
2pm
3pm
4pm
5pm
6pm
7pm

▷ AFFIRMATIONS

▷ SALES GOALS

▷ NOTES / IDEAS

DATE

M   T   W   Th   F   Sa   Su

TODAY'S TOP 3

To Do

- ☐
- ☐
- ☐
- ☐
- ☐
- ☐
- ☐
- ☐
- ☐
- ☐

Income Generating Activities

APPOINTMENTS

6am

7am

8am

9am

10am

11am

12pm

1pm

2pm

3pm

4pm

5pm

6pm

7pm

AFFIRMATIONS

SALES GOALS

NOTES / IDEAS

DATE

M   T   W   Th   F   Sa   Su

TODAY'S TOP 3

To Do	Income Generating Activities
☐	
☐	
☐	
☐	
☐	
☐	
☐	
☐	
☐	
☐	

APPOINTMENTS

6am

7am

8am

9am

10am

11am

12pm

1pm

2pm

3pm

4pm

5pm

6pm

7pm

AFFIRMATIONS

SALES GOALS

NOTES / IDEAS

DATE

M   T   W   Th   F   Sa   Su

▷ _____
▷ _____
▷ _____

TODAY'S TOP 3

To Do

- ☐ _____
- ☐ _____
- ☐ _____
- ☐ _____
- ☐ _____
- ☐ _____
- ☐ _____
- ☐ _____
- ☐ _____
- ☐ _____
- ☐ _____

Income Generating Activities

APPOINTMENTS

6am	
7am	
8am	
9am	
10am	
11am	
12pm	
1pm	
2pm	
3pm	
4pm	
5pm	
6pm	
7pm	

▷ AFFIRMATIONS

▷ SALES GOALS

▷ NOTES / IDEAS

THIS WEEK IN REVIEW

This Week's Big Wins

- [ ]
- [ ]
- [ ]
- [ ]
- [ ]
- [ ]
- [ ]
- [ ]

NOTES

NEXT WEEK AT A GLANCE

MON

TUE

WED

THU

FRI

SAT

SUN

DATE

M　T　W　Th　F　Sa　Su

▷ _____

▷ _____

▷ _____

TODAY'S TOP 3

To Do

- ☐ _____
- ☐ _____
- ☐ _____
- ☐ _____
- ☐ _____
- ☐ _____
- ☐ _____
- ☐ _____
- ☐ _____
- ☐ _____
- ☐ _____

Income Generating Activities

_____

_____

_____

_____

_____

_____

_____

_____

_____

_____

APPOINTMENTS

6am	
7am	
8am	
9am	
10am	
11am	
12pm	
1pm	
2pm	
3pm	
4pm	
5pm	
6pm	
7pm	

▷ AFFIRMATIONS

▷ SALES GOALS

▷ NOTES / IDEAS

DATE   M   T   W   Th   F   Sa   Su

▷ _____

▷ _____

▷ _____

To Do

☐ _____

☐ _____

☐ _____

☐ _____

☐ _____

☐ _____

☐ _____

☐ _____

☐ _____

☐ _____

Income Generating Activities

APPOINTMENTS

6am _____

7am _____

8am _____

9am _____

10am _____

11am _____

12pm _____

1pm _____

2pm _____

3pm _____

4pm _____

5pm _____

6pm _____

7pm _____

▷ **AFFIRMATIONS**

▷ **SALES GOALS**

▷ **NOTES / IDEAS**

DATE

M   T   W   Th   F   Sa   Su

≫ ....

≫ ....

≫ ....

TODAY'S TOP 3

To Do

- ☐ ....
- ☐ ....
- ☐ ....
- ☐ ....
- ☐ ....
- ☐ ....
- ☐ ....
- ☐ ....
- ☐ ....
- ☐ ....
- ☐ ....

Income Generating Activities

APPOINTMENTS

6am

7am

8am

9am

10am

11am

12pm

1pm

2pm

3pm

4pm

5pm

6pm

7pm

≫ AFFIRMATIONS

≫ SALES GOALS

≫ NOTES / IDEAS

DATE

M   T   W   Th   F   Sa   Su

TODAY'S TOP 3

To Do

- ☐
- ☐
- ☐
- ☐
- ☐
- ☐
- ☐
- ☐
- ☐
- ☐

Income Generating Activities

APPOINTMENTS

6am
7am
8am
9am
10am
11am
12pm
1pm
2pm
3pm
4pm
5pm
6pm
7pm

AFFIRMATIONS

SALES GOALS

NOTES / IDEAS

DATE

M   T   W   Th   F   Sa   Su

▷
▷
▷

TODAY'S TOP 3

To Do

- ☐
- ☐
- ☐
- ☐
- ☐
- ☐
- ☐
- ☐
- ☐
- ☐

Income Generating Activities

APPOINTMENTS

6am
7am
8am
9am
10am
11am
12pm
1pm
2pm
3pm
4pm
5pm
6pm
7pm

▷ AFFIRMATIONS

▷ SALES GOALS

▷ NOTES / IDEAS

DATE

M T W Th F Sa Su

TODAY'S TOP 3

▷ ....

▷ ....

▷ ....

To Do

☐
☐
☐
☐
☐
☐
☐
☐
☐
☐

Income Generating Activities

APPOINTMENTS

6am

7am

8am

9am

10am

11am

12pm

1pm

2pm

3pm

4pm

5pm

6pm

7pm

▷ AFFIRMATIONS

▷ SALES GOALS

▷ NOTES / IDEAS

DATE

M   T   W   Th   F   Sa   Su

▷

▷

▷

TODAY'S TOP 3

To Do

☐
☐
☐
☐
☐
☐
☐
☐
☐
☐

Income Generating Activities

APPOINTMENTS

6am
7am
8am
9am
10am
11am
12pm
1pm
2pm
3pm
4pm
5pm
6pm
7pm

▷ AFFIRMATIONS

▷ SALES GOALS

▷ NOTES / IDEAS

THIS WEEK IN REVIEW
This Week's Big Wins

☐ _____

☐ _____

☐ _____

☐ _____

☐ _____

☐ _____

☐ _____

NOTES

MON

NEXT WEEK AT A GLANCE

TUE

WED

THU

FRI

SAT

SUN

DATE

M   T   W   Th   F   Sa   Su

➤
➤
➤

TODAY'S TOP 3

To Do

☐
☐
☐
☐
☐
☐
☐
☐
☐
☐

Income Generating Activities

APPOINTMENTS

6am	
7am	➤ **AFFIRMATIONS**
8am	
9am	
10am	
11am	➤ **SALES GOALS**
12pm	
1pm	
2pm	
3pm	
4pm	➤ **NOTES / IDEAS**
5pm	
6pm	
7pm	

DATE

M T W Th F Sa Su

To Do

- [ ]
- [ ]
- [ ]
- [ ]
- [ ]
- [ ]
- [ ]
- [ ]
- [ ]
- [ ]

Income Generating Activities

APPOINTMENTS

6am	
7am	
8am	
9am	
10am	
11am	
12pm	
1pm	
2pm	
3pm	
4pm	
5pm	
6pm	
7pm	

AFFIRMATIONS

SALES GOALS

NOTES / IDEAS

DATE

M   T   W   Th   F   Sa   Su

TODAY'S TOP 3

To Do

- [ ]
- [ ]
- [ ]
- [ ]
- [ ]
- [ ]
- [ ]
- [ ]
- [ ]
- [ ]

Income Generating Activities

APPOINTMENTS

6am	
7am	
8am	
9am	
10am	
11am	
12pm	
1pm	
2pm	
3pm	
4pm	
5pm	
6pm	
7pm	

AFFIRMATIONS

SALES GOALS

NOTES / IDEAS

DATE

M   T   W   Th   F   Sa   Su

To Do

- [ ]
- [ ]
- [ ]
- [ ]
- [ ]
- [ ]
- [ ]
- [ ]
- [ ]
- [ ]

Income Generating Activities

APPOINTMENTS

6am
7am
8am
9am
10am
11am
12pm
1pm
2pm
3pm
4pm
5pm
6pm
7pm

AFFIRMATIONS

SALES GOALS

NOTES / IDEAS

DATE			M	T	W	Th	F	Sa	Su

≫ ....

≫ ....

≫ ....

To Do

- ☐
- ☐
- ☐
- ☐
- ☐
- ☐
- ☐
- ☐
- ☐
- ☐

Income Generating Activities

APPOINTMENTS

6am

7am

8am

9am

10am

11am

12pm

1pm

2pm

3pm

4pm

5pm

6pm

7pm

≫ AFFIRMATIONS

≫ SALES GOALS

≫ NOTES / IDEAS

DATE

M T W Th F Sa Su

▷ ....

▷ ....

▷ ....

To Do

- ☐
- ☐
- ☐
- ☐
- ☐
- ☐
- ☐
- ☐
- ☐
- ☐

Income Generating Activities

APPOINTMENTS

6am

7am

8am

9am

10am

11am

12pm

1pm

2pm

3pm

4pm

5pm

6pm

7pm

▷ AFFIRMATIONS

▷ SALES GOALS

▷ NOTES / IDEAS

DATE

M   T   W   Th   F   Sa   Su

TODAY'S TOP 3

To Do

- [ ]
- [ ]
- [ ]
- [ ]
- [ ]
- [ ]
- [ ]
- [ ]
- [ ]
- [ ]

Income Generating Activities

APPOINTMENTS

6am	
7am	
8am	
9am	
10am	
11am	
12pm	
1pm	
2pm	
3pm	
4pm	
5pm	
6pm	
7pm	

AFFIRMATIONS

SALES GOALS

NOTES / IDEAS

THIS WEEK IN REVIEW
This Week's Big Wins

☐ _____

☐ _____

☐ _____

☐ _____

☐ _____

☐ _____

☐ _____

NOTES

_____

_____

_____

_____

_____

_____

_____

MON _____

NEXT WEEK AT A GLANCE

TUE _____

WED _____

THU _____

FRI _____

SAT _____

SUN _____

DATE

M   T   W   Th   F   Sa   Su

▷ _____

▷ _____

▷ _____

TODAY'S TOP 3

To Do

- ☐ _____
- ☐ _____
- ☐ _____
- ☐ _____
- ☐ _____
- ☐ _____
- ☐ _____
- ☐ _____
- ☐ _____
- ☐ _____
- ☐ _____

Income Generating Activities

APPOINTMENTS

6am _____

7am _____

8am _____

9am _____

10am _____

11am _____

12pm _____

1pm _____

2pm _____

3pm _____

4pm _____

5pm _____

6pm _____

7pm _____

▷ AFFIRMATIONS

▷ SALES GOALS

▷ NOTES / IDEAS

DATE   M   T   W   Th   F   Sa   Su

TODAY'S TOP 3

▷

▷

▷

To Do

- ☐
- ☐
- ☐
- ☐
- ☐
- ☐
- ☐
- ☐
- ☐
- ☐

Income Generating Activities

APPOINTMENTS

6am

7am

8am

9am

10am

11am

12pm

1pm

2pm

3pm

4pm

5pm

6pm

7pm

▷ AFFIRMATIONS

▷ SALES GOALS

▷ NOTES / IDEAS

DATE

M   T   W   Th   F   Sa   Su

TODAY'S TOP 3

▷
▷
▷

To Do

☐
☐
☐
☐
☐
☐
☐
☐
☐
☐

Income Generating Activities

APPOINTMENTS

6am
7am
8am
9am
10am
11am
12pm
1pm
2pm
3pm
4pm
5pm
6pm
7pm

▷ AFFIRMATIONS

▷ SALES GOALS

▷ NOTES / IDEAS

DATE

M T W Th F Sa Su

▶
▶
▶

To Do

☐
☐
☐
☐
☐
☐
☐
☐
☐
☐

Income Generating Activities

APPOINTMENTS

6am
7am
8am
9am
10am
11am
12pm
1pm
2pm
3pm
4pm
5pm
6pm
7pm

▶ AFFIRMATIONS

▶ SALES GOALS

▶ NOTES / IDEAS

DATE

M   T   W   Th   F   Sa   Su

▷

▷

▷

TODAY'S TOP 3

To Do

- ☐
- ☐
- ☐
- ☐
- ☐
- ☐
- ☐
- ☐
- ☐
- ☐
- ☐

Income Generating Activities

APPOINTMENTS

6am

7am

8am

9am

10am

11am

12pm

1pm

2pm

3pm

4pm

5pm

6pm

7pm

▷ AFFIRMATIONS

▷ SALES GOALS

▷ NOTES / IDEAS

DATE

M T W Th F Sa Su

TODAY'S TOP 3

▷ _____

▷ _____

▷ _____

To Do

☐ _____
☐ _____
☐ _____
☐ _____
☐ _____
☐ _____
☐ _____
☐ _____
☐ _____
☐ _____

Income Generating Activities

APPOINTMENTS

6am	
7am	
8am	
9am	
10am	
11am	
12pm	
1pm	
2pm	
3pm	
4pm	
5pm	
6pm	
7pm	

▷ AFFIRMATIONS

▷ SALES GOALS

▷ NOTES / IDEAS

DATE

M   T   W   Th   F   Sa   Su

▷ _____

▷ _____

▷ _____

TODAY'S TOP 3

To Do

- ☐ _____
- ☐ _____
- ☐ _____
- ☐ _____
- ☐ _____
- ☐ _____
- ☐ _____
- ☐ _____
- ☐ _____
- ☐ _____
- ☐ _____

Income Generating Activities

APPOINTMENTS

6am	
7am	
8am	
9am	
10am	
11am	
12pm	
1pm	
2pm	
3pm	
4pm	
5pm	
6pm	
7pm	

▷ AFFIRMATIONS

▷ SALES GOALS

▷ NOTES / IDEAS

THIS WEEK IN REVIEW

This Week's Big Wins

- ☐
- ☐
- ☐
- ☐
- ☐
- ☐
- ☐
- ☐

NOTES

NEXT WEEK AT A GLANCE

MON

TUE

WED

THU

FRI

SAT

SUN

_____ MONTH IN REVIEW

MONTHLY WINS

▷
▷

▷
▷

▷
▷

▷
▷

INCOME GENERATING HABITS THAT SUPPORT MONTHLY GOALS

▷   ☐ DAILY HABIT   ☐ WEEKLY HABIT

▷   ☐ DAILY HABIT   ☐ WEEKLY HABIT

▷   ☐ DAILY HABIT   ☐ WEEKLY HABIT

▷   ☐ DAILY HABIT   ☐ WEEKLY HABIT

▷   ☐ DAILY HABIT   ☐ WEEKLY HABIT

DAILY SALES

1.	11.	21.
2.	12.	22.
3.	13.	23.
4.	14.	24.
5.	15.	25.
6.	16.	26.
7.	17.	27.
8.	18.	28.
9.	19.	29.
10.	20.	30.

▷ *When you feel like quitting, think about why you started.*

No
Limits

MONTH _____

SUNDAY	MONDAY	TUESDAY	WEDNESDAY

Luck is what happens when preparation meets opportunity.
– Darryl Royal

THURSDAY	FRIDAY	SATURDAY	NOTES

DATE

M T W Th F Sa Su

▷
▷
▷

To Do

- ☐
- ☐
- ☐
- ☐
- ☐
- ☐
- ☐
- ☐
- ☐
- ☐
- ☐

Income Generating Activities

APPOINTMENTS

6am	
7am	
8am	
9am	
10am	
11am	
12pm	
1pm	
2pm	
3pm	
4pm	
5pm	
6pm	
7pm	

▷ AFFIRMATIONS

▷ SALES GOALS

▷ NOTES / IDEAS

DATE

M   T   W   Th   F   Sa   Su

▷ _____
▷ _____
▷ _____

TODAY'S TOP 3

To Do

☐ _____
☐ _____
☐ _____
☐ _____
☐ _____
☐ _____
☐ _____
☐ _____
☐ _____
☐ _____

Income Generating Activities

APPOINTMENTS

6am _____
7am _____
8am _____
9am _____
10am _____
11am _____
12pm _____
1pm _____
2pm _____
3pm _____
4pm _____
5pm _____
6pm _____
7pm _____

▷ AFFIRMATIONS

▷ SALES GOALS

▷ NOTES / IDEAS

DATE

M   T   W   Th   F   Sa   Su

> _____

> _____

> _____

TODAY'S TOP 3

To Do

- [ ] _____
- [ ] _____
- [ ] _____
- [ ] _____
- [ ] _____
- [ ] _____
- [ ] _____
- [ ] _____
- [ ] _____
- [ ] _____

Income Generating Activities

APPOINTMENTS

6am	
7am	
8am	
9am	
10am	
11am	
12pm	
1pm	
2pm	
3pm	
4pm	
5pm	
6pm	
7pm	

> AFFIRMATIONS

> SALES GOALS

> NOTES / IDEAS

DATE

M　T　W　Th　F　Sa　Su

▷ _____

▷ _____

▷ _____

To Do

- ☐ _____
- ☐ _____
- ☐ _____
- ☐ _____
- ☐ _____
- ☐ _____
- ☐ _____
- ☐ _____
- ☐ _____
- ☐ _____

Income Generating Activities

_____

_____

_____

_____

_____

_____

_____

_____

_____

APPOINTMENTS

6am _____

7am _____

8am _____

9am _____

10am _____

11am _____

12pm _____

1pm _____

2pm _____

3pm _____

4pm _____

5pm _____

6pm _____

7pm _____

▷ AFFIRMATIONS

▷ SALES GOALS

▷ NOTES / IDEAS

TODAY'S TOP 3

To Do

- ☐
- ☐
- ☐
- ☐
- ☐
- ☐
- ☐
- ☐
- ☐
- ☐
- ☐

Income Generating Activities

APPOINTMENTS

6am
7am
8am
9am
10am
11am
12pm
1pm
2pm
3pm
4pm
5pm
6pm
7pm

AFFIRMATIONS

SALES GOALS

NOTES / IDEAS

DATE

M T W Th F Sa Su

▷
▷
▷

TODAY'S TOP 3

To Do

☐
☐
☐
☐
☐
☐
☐
☐
☐
☐

Income Generating Activities

APPOINTMENTS

6am	
7am	
8am	
9am	
10am	
11am	
12pm	
1pm	
2pm	
3pm	
4pm	
5pm	
6pm	
7pm	

▷ AFFIRMATIONS

▷ SALES GOALS

▷ NOTES / IDEAS

DATE

M   T   W   Th   F   Sa   Su

TODAY'S TOP 3

➤

➤

➤

To Do

☐

☐

☐

☐

☐

☐

☐

☐

☐

☐

Income Generating Activities

APPOINTMENTS

| 6am |
| 7am |
| 8am |
| 9am |
| 10am |
| 11am |
| 12pm |
| 1pm |
| 2pm |
| 3pm |
| 4pm |
| 5pm |
| 6pm |
| 7pm |

➤ AFFIRMATIONS

➤ SALES GOALS

➤ NOTES / IDEAS

THIS WEEK IN REVIEW

This Week's Big Wins

- ☐ _____
- ☐ _____
- ☐ _____
- ☐ _____
- ☐ _____
- ☐ _____
- ☐ _____
- ☐ _____

NOTES

NEXT WEEK AT A GLANCE

MON

TUE

WED

THU

FRI

SAT

SUN

DATE

M	T	W	Th	F	Sa	Su

▷

▷

▷

To Do

- ☐
- ☐
- ☐
- ☐
- ☐
- ☐
- ☐
- ☐
- ☐
- ☐

Income Generating Activities

APPOINTMENTS

6am

7am

8am

9am

10am

11am

12pm

1pm

2pm

3pm

4pm

5pm

6pm

7pm

▷ AFFIRMATIONS

▷ SALES GOALS

▷ NOTES / IDEAS

DATE

M T W Th F Sa Su

▷ _____

▷ _____

▷ _____

TODAY'S TOP 3

To Do

- ☐ _____
- ☐ _____
- ☐ _____
- ☐ _____
- ☐ _____
- ☐ _____
- ☐ _____
- ☐ _____
- ☐ _____
- ☐ _____

Income Generating Activities

APPOINTMENTS

6am
7am
8am
9am
10am
11am
12pm
1pm
2pm
3pm
4pm
5pm
6pm
7pm

▷ AFFIRMATIONS

▷ SALES GOALS

▷ NOTES / IDEAS

DATE

M   T   W   Th   F   Sa   Su

▷ _____

▷ _____

▷ _____

TODAY'S TOP 3

To Do

- ☐ _____
- ☐ _____
- ☐ _____
- ☐ _____
- ☐ _____
- ☐ _____
- ☐ _____
- ☐ _____
- ☐ _____
- ☐ _____

Income Generating Activities

APPOINTMENTS

6am

7am

8am

9am

10am

11am

12pm

1pm

2pm

3pm

4pm

5pm

6pm

7pm

▷ AFFIRMATIONS

▷ SALES GOALS

▷ NOTES / IDEAS

DATE

M   T   W   Th   F   Sa   Su

▷ _____

▷ _____

▷ _____

TODAY'S TOP 3

To Do

- ☐ _____
- ☐ _____
- ☐ _____
- ☐ _____
- ☐ _____
- ☐ _____
- ☐ _____
- ☐ _____
- ☐ _____
- ☐ _____

Income Generating Activities

_____

_____

_____

_____

_____

_____

_____

_____

_____

APPOINTMENTS

6am

7am

8am

9am

10am

11am

12pm

1pm

2pm

3pm

4pm

5pm

6pm

7pm

▷ AFFIRMATIONS

▷ SALES GOALS

▷ NOTES / IDEAS

DATE

M   T   W   Th   F   Sa   Su

▷ ....

▷ ....

▷ ....

TODAY'S TOP 3

To Do

☐ ....
☐ ....
☐ ....
☐ ....
☐ ....
☐ ....
☐ ....
☐ ....
☐ ....
☐ ....

Income Generating Activities

APPOINTMENTS

6am
7am
8am
9am
10am
11am
12pm
1pm
2pm
3pm
4pm
5pm
6pm
7pm

▷ AFFIRMATIONS

▷ SALES GOALS

▷ NOTES / IDEAS

DATE

M   T   W   Th   F   Sa   Su

▷ ....

▷ ....

▷ ....

TODAY'S TOP 3

To Do

- ☐ ....
- ☐ ....
- ☐ ....
- ☐ ....
- ☐ ....
- ☐ ....
- ☐ ....
- ☐ ....
- ☐ ....
- ☐ ....

Income Generating Activities

APPOINTMENTS

6am
7am
8am
9am
10am
11am
12pm
1pm
2pm
3pm
4pm
5pm
6pm
7pm

▷ AFFIRMATIONS

▷ SALES GOALS

▷ NOTES / IDEAS

DATE

▷ _____

▷ _____

▷ _____

TODAY'S TOP 3

To Do

- ☐ _____
- ☐ _____
- ☐ _____
- ☐ _____
- ☐ _____
- ☐ _____
- ☐ _____
- ☐ _____
- ☐ _____
- ☐ _____

Income Generating Activities

_____

_____

_____

_____

_____

_____

_____

_____

APPOINTMENTS

6am

7am

8am

9am

10am

11am

12pm

1pm

2pm

3pm

4pm

5pm

6pm

7pm

▷ AFFIRMATIONS

▷ SALES GOALS

▷ NOTES / IDEAS

THIS WEEK IN REVIEW

This Week's Big Wins

- [ ] _____
- [ ] _____
- [ ] _____
- [ ] _____
- [ ] _____
- [ ] _____
- [ ] _____
- [ ] _____

NOTES

_____

_____

_____

_____

_____

_____

_____

NEXT WEEK AT A GLANCE

MON _____

TUE _____

WED _____

THU _____

FRI _____

SAT _____

SUN _____

DATE

M   T   W   Th   F   Sa   Su

▷ _____

▷ _____

▷ _____

TODAY'S TOP 3

To Do

- ☐ _____
- ☐ _____
- ☐ _____
- ☐ _____
- ☐ _____
- ☐ _____
- ☐ _____
- ☐ _____
- ☐ _____
- ☐ _____

Income Generating Activities

APPOINTMENTS

6am

7am

8am

9am

10am

11am

12pm

1pm

2pm

3pm

4pm

5pm

6pm

7pm

▷ AFFIRMATIONS

▷ SALES GOALS

▷ NOTES / IDEAS

DATE

M T W Th F Sa Su

TODAY'S TOP 3

▷
▷
▷

To Do

☐
☐
☐
☐
☐
☐
☐
☐
☐
☐

Income Generating Activities

APPOINTMENTS

6am
7am
8am
9am
10am
11am
12pm
1pm
2pm
3pm
4pm
5pm
6pm
7pm

▷ AFFIRMATIONS

▷ SALES GOALS

▷ NOTES / IDEAS

DATE

M   T   W   Th   F   Sa   Su

▷ _____

▷ _____

▷ _____

To Do

- ☐ _____
- ☐ _____
- ☐ _____
- ☐ _____
- ☐ _____
- ☐ _____
- ☐ _____
- ☐ _____
- ☐ _____
- ☐ _____

Income Generating Activities

_____

_____

_____

_____

_____

_____

_____

_____

_____

_____

_____

APPOINTMENTS

6am _____

7am _____

8am _____

9am _____

10am _____

11am _____

12pm _____

1pm _____

2pm _____

3pm _____

4pm _____

5pm _____

6pm _____

7pm _____

▷ AFFIRMATIONS

▷ SALES GOALS

▷ NOTES / IDEAS

DATE

M   T   W   Th   F   Sa   Su

▷

▷

▷

TODAY'S TOP 3

To Do

- ☐
- ☐
- ☐
- ☐
- ☐
- ☐
- ☐
- ☐
- ☐
- ☐

Income Generating Activities

APPOINTMENTS

6am	
7am	
8am	
9am	
10am	
11am	
12pm	
1pm	
2pm	
3pm	
4pm	
5pm	
6pm	
7pm	

▷ AFFIRMATIONS

▷ SALES GOALS

▷ NOTES / IDEAS

DATE

M   T   W   Th   F   Sa   Su

▷

▷

▷

TODAY'S TOP 3

To Do

- ☐
- ☐
- ☐
- ☐
- ☐
- ☐
- ☐
- ☐
- ☐
- ☐

Income Generating Activities

APPOINTMENTS

6am	
7am	
8am	
9am	
10am	
11am	
12pm	
1pm	
2pm	
3pm	
4pm	
5pm	
6pm	
7pm	

▷ AFFIRMATIONS

▷ SALES GOALS

▷ NOTES / IDEAS

DATE

M T W Th F Sa Su

▷ _____

▷ _____

▷ _____

TODAY'S TOP 3

To Do

☐ _____
☐ _____
☐ _____
☐ _____
☐ _____
☐ _____
☐ _____
☐ _____
☐ _____
☐ _____

Income Generating Activities

APPOINTMENTS

6am
7am
8am
9am
10am
11am
12pm
1pm
2pm
3pm
4pm
5pm
6pm
7pm

▷ AFFIRMATIONS

▷ SALES GOALS

▷ NOTES / IDEAS

DATE

M   T   W   Th   F   Sa   Su

▷

▷

▷

TODAY'S TOP 3

To Do

☐
☐
☐
☐
☐
☐
☐
☐
☐
☐

Income Generating Activities

APPOINTMENTS

6am
7am
8am
9am
10am
11am
12pm
1pm
2pm
3pm
4pm
5pm
6pm
7pm

▷ AFFIRMATIONS

▷ SALES GOALS

▷ NOTES / IDEAS

THIS WEEK IN REVIEW

This Week's Big Wins

- ☐ _____
- ☐ _____
- ☐ _____
- ☐ _____
- ☐ _____
- ☐ _____
- ☐ _____
- ☐ _____

NOTES

_____

_____

_____

_____

_____

_____

_____

NEXT WEEK AT A GLANCE

MON _____

TUE _____

WED _____

THU _____

FRI _____

SAT _____

SUN _____

DATE

M   T   W   Th   F   Sa   Su

▷ ....

▷ ....

▷ ....

TODAY'S TOP 3

To Do

- [ ]
- [ ]
- [ ]
- [ ]
- [ ]
- [ ]
- [ ]
- [ ]
- [ ]
- [ ]

Income Generating Activities

APPOINTMENTS

6am	
7am	
8am	
9am	
10am	
11am	
12pm	
1pm	
2pm	
3pm	
4pm	
5pm	
6pm	
7pm	

▷ AFFIRMATIONS

▷ SALES GOALS

▷ NOTES / IDEAS

DATE

M T W Th F Sa Su

TODAY'S TOP 3

▷
▷
▷

To Do

☐
☐
☐
☐
☐
☐
☐
☐
☐
☐

Income Generating Activities

APPOINTMENTS

6am
7am
8am
9am
10am
11am
12pm
1pm
2pm
3pm
4pm
5pm
6pm
7pm

▷ AFFIRMATIONS

▷ SALES GOALS

▷ NOTES / IDEAS

DATE

M   T   W   Th   F   Sa   Su

▷ _____

▷ _____

▷ _____

TODAY'S TOP 3

To Do

- ☐ _____
- ☐ _____
- ☐ _____
- ☐ _____
- ☐ _____
- ☐ _____
- ☐ _____
- ☐ _____
- ☐ _____
- ☐ _____

Income Generating Activities

APPOINTMENTS

6am

7am

8am

9am

10am

11am

12pm

1pm

2pm

3pm

4pm

5pm

6pm

7pm

▷ AFFIRMATIONS

▷ SALES GOALS

▷ NOTES / IDEAS

DATE

M   T   W   Th   F   Sa   Su

TODAY'S TOP 3

To Do

- [ ]
- [ ]
- [ ]
- [ ]
- [ ]
- [ ]
- [ ]
- [ ]
- [ ]
- [ ]

Income Generating Activities

APPOINTMENTS

6am

7am

8am

9am

10am

11am

12pm

1pm

2pm

3pm

4pm

5pm

6pm

7pm

AFFIRMATIONS

SALES GOALS

NOTES / IDEAS

DATE

M   T   W   Th   F   Sa   Su

▷

▷

▷

TODAY'S TOP 3

To Do

- [ ]
- [ ]
- [ ]
- [ ]
- [ ]
- [ ]
- [ ]
- [ ]
- [ ]
- [ ]

Income Generating Activities

APPOINTMENTS

6am	
7am	
8am	
9am	
10am	
11am	
12pm	
1pm	
2pm	
3pm	
4pm	
5pm	
6pm	
7pm	

▷ AFFIRMATIONS

▷ SALES GOALS

▷ NOTES / IDEAS

DATE

M T W Th F Sa Su

TODAY'S TOP 3

To Do

- [ ]
- [ ]
- [ ]
- [ ]
- [ ]
- [ ]
- [ ]
- [ ]
- [ ]
- [ ]

Income Generating Activities

APPOINTMENTS

6am	
7am	
8am	
9am	
10am	
11am	
12pm	
1pm	
2pm	
3pm	
4pm	
5pm	
6pm	
7pm	

AFFIRMATIONS

SALES GOALS

NOTES / IDEAS

DATE

M T W Th F Sa Su

To Do

- [ ]
- [ ]
- [ ]
- [ ]
- [ ]
- [ ]
- [ ]
- [ ]
- [ ]
- [ ]

Income Generating Activities

APPOINTMENTS

6am	
7am	
8am	
9am	
10am	
11am	
12pm	
1pm	
2pm	
3pm	
4pm	
5pm	
6pm	
7pm	

AFFIRMATIONS

SALES GOALS

NOTES / IDEAS

THIS WEEK IN REVIEW

This Week's Big Wins

- ☐ _____
- ☐ _____
- ☐ _____
- ☐ _____
- ☐ _____
- ☐ _____
- ☐ _____
- ☐ _____

NOTES

_____

_____

_____

_____

_____

_____

MON

NEXT WEEK AT A GLANCE

TUE

WED

THU

FRI

SAT

SUN

DATE

M   T   W   Th   F   Sa   Su

▷ ....

▷ ....

▷ ....

TODAY'S TOP 3

To Do

- ☐
- ☐
- ☐
- ☐
- ☐
- ☐
- ☐
- ☐
- ☐
- ☐
- ☐

Income Generating Activities

APPOINTMENTS

| 6am |
| 7am |
| 8am |
| 9am |
| 10am |
| 11am |
| 12pm |
| 1pm |
| 2pm |
| 3pm |
| 4pm |
| 5pm |
| 6pm |
| 7pm |

▷ AFFIRMATIONS

▷ SALES GOALS

▷ NOTES / IDEAS

DATE

M   T   W   Th   F   Sa   Su

▷
▷
▷

TODAY'S TOP 3

To Do

☐
☐
☐
☐
☐
☐
☐
☐
☐
☐

Income Generating Activities

APPOINTMENTS

6am
7am
8am
9am
10am
11am
12pm
1pm
2pm
3pm
4pm
5pm
6pm
7pm

▷ AFFIRMATIONS

▷ SALES GOALS

▷ NOTES / IDEAS

DATE

M   T   W   Th   F   Sa   Su

TODAY'S TOP 3

To Do

- [ ]
- [ ]
- [ ]
- [ ]
- [ ]
- [ ]
- [ ]
- [ ]
- [ ]
- [ ]

Income Generating Activities

APPOINTMENTS

6am	
7am	
8am	
9am	
10am	
11am	
12pm	
1pm	
2pm	
3pm	
4pm	
5pm	
6pm	
7pm	

AFFIRMATIONS

SALES GOALS

NOTES / IDEAS

DATE

M   T   W   Th   F   Sa   Su

TODAY'S TOP 3

▷ ....

▷ ....

▷ ....

To Do

- ☐
- ☐
- ☐
- ☐
- ☐
- ☐
- ☐
- ☐
- ☐
- ☐

Income Generating Activities

APPOINTMENTS

| 6am |
| 7am |
| 8am |
| 9am |
| 10am |
| 11am |
| 12pm |
| 1pm |
| 2pm |
| 3pm |
| 4pm |
| 5pm |
| 6pm |
| 7pm |

▷ AFFIRMATIONS

▷ SALES GOALS

▷ NOTES / IDEAS

DATE

M   T   W   Th   F   Sa   Su

▷ ....

▷ ....

▷ ....

TODAY'S TOP 3

To Do

☐ ....

☐ ....

☐ ....

☐ ....

☐ ....

☐ ....

☐ ....

☐ ....

☐ ....

☐ ....

Income Generating Activities

APPOINTMENTS

6am ....

7am ....

8am ....

9am ....

10am ....

11am ....

12pm ....

1pm ....

2pm ....

3pm ....

4pm ....

5pm ....

6pm ....

7pm ....

▷ AFFIRMATIONS

▷ SALES GOALS

▷ NOTES / IDEAS

DATE

M   T   W   Th   F   Sa   Su

TODAY'S TOP 3

To Do

- [ ]
- [ ]
- [ ]
- [ ]
- [ ]
- [ ]
- [ ]
- [ ]
- [ ]
- [ ]

Income Generating Activities

APPOINTMENTS

6am	
7am	
8am	
9am	
10am	
11am	
12pm	
1pm	
2pm	
3pm	
4pm	
5pm	
6pm	
7pm	

AFFIRMATIONS

SALES GOALS

NOTES / IDEAS

DATE

M   T   W   Th   F   Sa   Su

▷

▷

▷

To Do

☐

☐

☐

☐

☐

☐

☐

☐

☐

☐

Income Generating Activities

APPOINTMENTS

6am

7am

8am

9am

10am

11am

12pm

1pm

2pm

3pm

4pm

5pm

6pm

7pm

▷ AFFIRMATIONS

▷ SALES GOALS

▷ NOTES / IDEAS

THIS WEEK IN REVIEW

This Week's Big Wins

☐ _____

☐ _____

☐ _____

☐ _____

☐ _____

☐ _____

☐ _____

NOTES

_____

_____

_____

_____

_____

_____

NEXT WEEK AT A GLANCE

MON _____

TUE _____

WED _____

THU _____

FRI _____

SAT _____

SUN _____

_____ MONTH IN REVIEW

MONTHLY WINS

▷ _____   ▷ _____

▷ _____   ▷ _____

▷ _____   ▷ _____

▷ _____   ▷ _____

INCOME GENERATING HABITS THAT SUPPORT MONTHLY GOALS

▷ _____   ☐ DAILY HABIT   ☐ WEEKLY HABIT

▷ _____   ☐ DAILY HABIT   ☐ WEEKLY HABIT

▷ _____   ☐ DAILY HABIT   ☐ WEEKLY HABIT

▷ _____   ☐ DAILY HABIT   ☐ WEEKLY HABIT

▷ _____   ☐ DAILY HABIT   ☐ WEEKLY HABIT

DAILY SALES

1. _____	11. _____	21. _____
2. _____	12. _____	22. _____
3. _____	13. _____	23. _____
4. _____	14. _____	24. _____
5. _____	15. _____	25. _____
6. _____	16. _____	26. _____
7. _____	17. _____	27. _____
8. _____	18. _____	28. _____
9. _____	19. _____	29. _____
10. _____	20. _____	30. _____

▷ *You are one day closer to accomplishing your goals.*

Focus, Focus, Focus

MONTH _____

SUNDAY	MONDAY	TUESDAY	WEDNESDAY

Believe in yourself and you will be unstoppable.

THURSDAY	FRIDAY	SATURDAY	NOTES

DATE

M   T   W   Th   F   Sa   Su

➤ _____

➤ _____

➤ _____

TODAY'S TOP 3

To Do

☐ _____

☐ _____

☐ _____

☐ _____

☐ _____

☐ _____

☐ _____

☐ _____

☐ _____

☐ _____

Income Generating Activities

APPOINTMENTS

6am

7am

8am

9am

10am

11am

12pm

1pm

2pm

3pm

4pm

5pm

6pm

7pm

➤ AFFIRMATIONS

➤ SALES GOALS

➤ NOTES / IDEAS

DATE

M T W Th F Sa Su

▷
▷
▷

TODAY'S TOP 3

To Do

☐
☐
☐
☐
☐
☐
☐
☐
☐
☐

Income Generating Activities

APPOINTMENTS

6am
7am
8am
9am
10am
11am
12pm
1pm
2pm
3pm
4pm
5pm
6pm
7pm

▷ AFFIRMATIONS

▷ SALES GOALS

▷ NOTES / IDEAS

DATE

M   T   W   Th   F   Sa   Su

▷

▷

▷

TODAY'S TOP 3

To Do

- ☐
- ☐
- ☐
- ☐
- ☐
- ☐
- ☐
- ☐
- ☐
- ☐

Income Generating Activities

APPOINTMENTS

6am

7am

8am

9am

10am

11am

12pm

1pm

2pm

3pm

4pm

5pm

6pm

7pm

▷ AFFIRMATIONS

▷ SALES GOALS

▷ NOTES / IDEAS

DATE

M   T   W   Th   F   Sa   Su

▷ _____

▷ _____

▷ _____

TODAY'S TOP 3

To Do

- ☐ _____
- ☐ _____
- ☐ _____
- ☐ _____
- ☐ _____
- ☐ _____
- ☐ _____
- ☐ _____
- ☐ _____
- ☐ _____

Income Generating Activities

APPOINTMENTS

6am

7am

8am

9am

10am

11am

12pm

1pm

2pm

3pm

4pm

5pm

6pm

7pm

▷ AFFIRMATIONS

▷ SALES GOALS

▷ NOTES / IDEAS

DATE   M   T   W   Th   F   Sa   Su

To Do

- [ ]
- [ ]
- [ ]
- [ ]
- [ ]
- [ ]
- [ ]
- [ ]
- [ ]
- [ ]

Income Generating Activities

APPOINTMENTS

6am
7am
8am
9am
10am
11am
12pm
1pm
2pm
3pm
4pm
5pm
6pm
7pm

AFFIRMATIONS

SALES GOALS

NOTES / IDEAS

DATE

M   T   W   Th   F   Sa   Su

▷
▷
▷

TODAY'S TOP 3

To Do

- ☐
- ☐
- ☐
- ☐
- ☐
- ☐
- ☐
- ☐
- ☐
- ☐
- ☐

Income Generating Activities

APPOINTMENTS

6am	
7am	
8am	
9am	
10am	
11am	
12pm	
1pm	
2pm	
3pm	
4pm	
5pm	
6pm	
7pm	

▷ AFFIRMATIONS

▷ SALES GOALS

▷ NOTES / IDEAS

DATE

M   T   W   Th   F   Sa   Su

▷ _____

▷ _____

▷ _____

To Do

- ☐
- ☐
- ☐
- ☐
- ☐
- ☐
- ☐
- ☐
- ☐
- ☐
- ☐

Income Generating Activities

APPOINTMENTS

6am

7am

8am

9am

10am

11am

12pm

1pm

2pm

3pm

4pm

5pm

6pm

7pm

▷ AFFIRMATIONS

▷ SALES GOALS

▷ NOTES / IDEAS

THIS WEEK IN REVIEW

This Week's Big Wins

- [ ]
- [ ]
- [ ]
- [ ]
- [ ]
- [ ]
- [ ]
- [ ]

NOTES

NEXT WEEK AT A GLANCE

MON

TUE

WED

THU

FRI

SAT

SUN

DATE

M   T   W   Th   F   Sa   Su

▷

▷

▷

TODAY'S TOP 3

To Do

☐

☐

☐

☐

☐

☐

☐

☐

☐

☐

☐

Income Generating Activities

APPOINTMENTS

6am	
7am	
8am	
9am	
10am	
11am	
12pm	
1pm	
2pm	
3pm	
4pm	
5pm	
6pm	
7pm	

▷ AFFIRMATIONS

▷ SALES GOALS

▷ NOTES / IDEAS

DATE

	M	T	W	Th	F	Sa	Su

▷ ....

▷ ....

▷ ....

TODAY'S TOP 3

To Do

☐ ....

☐ ....

☐ ....

☐ ....

☐ ....

☐ ....

☐ ....

☐ ....

☐ ....

☐ ....

Income Generating Activities

APPOINTMENTS

6am ....

7am ....

8am ....

9am ....

10am ....

11am ....

12pm ....

1pm ....

2pm ....

3pm ....

4pm ....

5pm ....

6pm ....

7pm ....

▷ AFFIRMATIONS

▷ SALES GOALS

▷ NOTES / IDEAS

DATE

M   T   W   Th   F   Sa   Su

TODAY'S TOP 3

▷ _____

▷ _____

▷ _____

To Do

- ☐ _____
- ☐ _____
- ☐ _____
- ☐ _____
- ☐ _____
- ☐ _____
- ☐ _____
- ☐ _____
- ☐ _____
- ☐ _____
- ☐ _____

Income Generating Activities

APPOINTMENTS

6am

7am

8am

9am

10am

11am

12pm

1pm

2pm

3pm

4pm

5pm

6pm

7pm

▷ AFFIRMATIONS

▷ SALES GOALS

▷ NOTES / IDEAS

DATE

M T W Th F Sa Su

▷ _____

▷ _____

▷ _____

To Do

- _____
- _____
- _____
- _____
- _____
- _____
- _____
- _____
- _____
- _____

Income Generating Activities

_____

_____

_____

_____

_____

_____

_____

_____

_____

APPOINTMENTS

6am
7am
8am
9am
10am
11am
12pm
1pm
2pm
3pm
4pm
5pm
6pm
7pm

▷ AFFIRMATIONS

▷ SALES GOALS

▷ NOTES / IDEAS

DATE

M   T   W   Th   F   Sa   Su

▷

▷

▷

TODAY'S TOP 3

To Do

- ☐
- ☐
- ☐
- ☐
- ☐
- ☐
- ☐
- ☐
- ☐
- ☐
- ☐

Income Generating Activities

APPOINTMENTS

6am	
7am	
8am	
9am	
10am	
11am	
12pm	
1pm	
2pm	
3pm	
4pm	
5pm	
6pm	
7pm	

▷ AFFIRMATIONS

▷ SALES GOALS

▷ NOTES / IDEAS

DATE

M   T   W   Th   F   Sa   Su

▷

▷

▷

TODAY'S TOP 3

To Do

☐

☐

☐

☐

☐

☐

☐

☐

☐

☐

Income Generating Activities

APPOINTMENTS

6am

7am

8am

9am

10am

11am

12pm

1pm

2pm

3pm

4pm

5pm

6pm

7pm

▷ AFFIRMATIONS

▷ SALES GOALS

▷ NOTES / IDEAS

DATE

M   T   W   Th   F   Sa   Su

▷
▷
▷

TODAY'S TOP 3

To Do

- ☐
- ☐
- ☐
- ☐
- ☐
- ☐
- ☐
- ☐
- ☐
- ☐
- ☐

Income Generating Activities

APPOINTMENTS

6am
7am
8am
9am
10am
11am
12pm
1pm
2pm
3pm
4pm
5pm
6pm
7pm

▷ AFFIRMATIONS

▷ SALES GOALS

▷ NOTES / IDEAS

THIS WEEK IN REVIEW

This Week's Big Wins

- ☐ _____
- ☐ _____
- ☐ _____
- ☐ _____
- ☐ _____
- ☐ _____
- ☐ _____

NOTES

_____
_____
_____
_____
_____
_____
_____

NEXT WEEK AT A GLANCE

MON
_____

TUE
_____

WED
_____

THU
_____

FRI
_____

SAT
_____

SUN
_____

DATE

M   T   W   Th   F   Sa   Su

TODAY'S TOP 3

To Do

- [ ]
- [ ]
- [ ]
- [ ]
- [ ]
- [ ]
- [ ]
- [ ]
- [ ]
- [ ]

Income Generating Activities

APPOINTMENTS

6am	
7am	
8am	
9am	
10am	
11am	
12pm	
1pm	
2pm	
3pm	
4pm	
5pm	
6pm	
7pm	

AFFIRMATIONS

SALES GOALS

NOTES / IDEAS

DATE

M T W Th F Sa Su

▷
▷
▷

TODAY'S TOP 3

To Do

☐
☐
☐
☐
☐
☐
☐
☐
☐
☐

Income Generating Activities

APPOINTMENTS

6am
7am
8am
9am
10am
11am
12pm
1pm
2pm
3pm
4pm
5pm
6pm
7pm

▷ AFFIRMATIONS

▷ SALES GOALS

▷ NOTES / IDEAS

DATE

M   T   W   Th   F   Sa   Su

▷

▷

▷

TODAY'S TOP 3

To Do

- ☐
- ☐
- ☐
- ☐
- ☐
- ☐
- ☐
- ☐
- ☐
- ☐
- ☐

Income Generating Activities

APPOINTMENTS

| 6am |
| 7am |
| 8am |
| 9am |
| 10am |
| 11am |
| 12pm |
| 1pm |
| 2pm |
| 3pm |
| 4pm |
| 5pm |
| 6pm |
| 7pm |

▷ AFFIRMATIONS

▷ SALES GOALS

▷ NOTES / IDEAS

DATE

M   T   W   Th   F   Sa   Su

TODAY'S TOP 3

▷ _____
▷ _____
▷ _____

To Do

☐ _____
☐ _____
☐ _____
☐ _____
☐ _____
☐ _____
☐ _____
☐ _____
☐ _____
☐ _____

Income Generating Activities

_____
_____
_____
_____
_____
_____
_____
_____
_____
_____

APPOINTMENTS

6am
7am
8am
9am
10am
11am
12pm
1pm
2pm
3pm
4pm
5pm
6pm
7pm

▷ AFFIRMATIONS

▷ SALES GOALS

▷ NOTES / IDEAS

DATE

M   T   W   Th   F   Sa   Su

TODAY'S TOP 3

To Do

- [ ]
- [ ]
- [ ]
- [ ]
- [ ]
- [ ]
- [ ]
- [ ]
- [ ]
- [ ]

Income Generating Activities

APPOINTMENTS

6am

7am

8am

9am

10am

11am

12pm

1pm

2pm

3pm

4pm

5pm

6pm

7pm

AFFIRMATIONS

SALES GOALS

NOTES / IDEAS

DATE | M   T   W   Th   F   Sa   Su

▷

▷

▷

TODAY'S TOP 3

To Do

- ☐
- ☐
- ☐
- ☐
- ☐
- ☐
- ☐
- ☐
- ☐
- ☐

Income Generating Activities

APPOINTMENTS

6am
7am
8am
9am
10am
11am
12pm
1pm
2pm
3pm
4pm
5pm
6pm
7pm

▷ AFFIRMATIONS

▷ SALES GOALS

▷ NOTES / IDEAS

DATE

▷
▷
▷

TODAY'S TOP 3

To Do

☐
☐
☐
☐
☐
☐
☐
☐
☐
☐
☐

Income Generating Activities

APPOINTMENTS

6am
7am
8am
9am
10am
11am
12pm
1pm
2pm
3pm
4pm
5pm
6pm
7pm

▷ AFFIRMATIONS

▷ SALES GOALS

▷ NOTES / IDEAS

THIS WEEK IN REVIEW
This Week's Big Wins

- [ ]
- [ ]
- [ ]
- [ ]
- [ ]
- [ ]
- [ ]

NOTES

NEXT WEEK AT A GLANCE

MON

TUE

WED

THU

FRI

SAT

SUN

DATE

M   T   W   Th   F   Sa   Su

TODAY'S TOP 3

To Do

- ☐
- ☐
- ☐
- ☐
- ☐
- ☐
- ☐
- ☐
- ☐
- ☐

Income Generating Activities

APPOINTMENTS

6am

7am

8am

9am

10am

11am

12pm

1pm

2pm

3pm

4pm

5pm

6pm

7pm

AFFIRMATIONS

SALES GOALS

NOTES / IDEAS

DATE

M   T   W   Th   F   Sa   Su

▷ ....

▷ ....

▷ ....

TODAY'S TOP 3

To Do

- ☐
- ☐
- ☐
- ☐
- ☐
- ☐
- ☐
- ☐
- ☐
- ☐

Income Generating Activities

APPOINTMENTS

6am	
7am	
8am	
9am	
10am	
11am	
12pm	
1pm	
2pm	
3pm	
4pm	
5pm	
6pm	
7pm	

▷ AFFIRMATIONS

▷ SALES GOALS

▷ NOTES / IDEAS

DATE

| | | M | T | W | Th | F | Sa | Su |

▷ _____

▷ _____

▷ _____

To Do

- ☐ _____
- ☐ _____
- ☐ _____
- ☐ _____
- ☐ _____
- ☐ _____
- ☐ _____
- ☐ _____
- ☐ _____
- ☐ _____
- ☐ _____

Income Generating Activities

APPOINTMENTS

6am	
7am	
8am	
9am	
10am	
11am	
12pm	
1pm	
2pm	
3pm	
4pm	
5pm	
6pm	
7pm	

▷ AFFIRMATIONS

▷ SALES GOALS

▷ NOTES / IDEAS

DATE

M T W Th F Sa Su

▷ ....

▷ ....

▷ ....

TODAY'S TOP 3

To Do

☐
☐
☐
☐
☐
☐
☐
☐
☐
☐

Income Generating Activities

APPOINTMENTS

6am
7am
8am
9am
10am
11am
12pm
1pm
2pm
3pm
4pm
5pm
6pm
7pm

▷ AFFIRMATIONS

▷ SALES GOALS

▷ NOTES / IDEAS

DATE

M   T   W   Th   F   Sa   Su

▷

▷

▷

TODAY'S TOP 3

To Do

- ☐
- ☐
- ☐
- ☐
- ☐
- ☐
- ☐
- ☐
- ☐
- ☐

Income Generating Activities

APPOINTMENTS

6am

7am

8am

9am

10am

11am

12pm

1pm

2pm

3pm

4pm

5pm

6pm

7pm

▷ AFFIRMATIONS

▷ SALES GOALS

▷ NOTES / IDEAS

DATE

M   T   W   Th   F   Sa   Su

TODAY'S TOP 3

▷ _____

▷ _____

▷ _____

To Do

- ☐ _____
- ☐ _____
- ☐ _____
- ☐ _____
- ☐ _____
- ☐ _____
- ☐ _____
- ☐ _____
- ☐ _____
- ☐ _____

Income Generating Activities

APPOINTMENTS

6am

7am

8am

9am

10am

11am

12pm

1pm

2pm

3pm

4pm

5pm

6pm

7pm

▷ AFFIRMATIONS

▷ SALES GOALS

▷ NOTES / IDEAS

DATE

M   T   W   Th   F   Sa   Su

▷ _____

▷ _____

▷ _____

TODAY'S TOP 3

To Do

- ☐ _____
- ☐ _____
- ☐ _____
- ☐ _____
- ☐ _____
- ☐ _____
- ☐ _____
- ☐ _____
- ☐ _____
- ☐ _____
- ☐ _____

Income Generating Activities

APPOINTMENTS

| 6am |
| 7am |
| 8am |
| 9am |
| 10am |
| 11am |
| 12pm |
| 1pm |
| 2pm |
| 3pm |
| 4pm |
| 5pm |
| 6pm |
| 7pm |

▷ AFFIRMATIONS

▷ SALES GOALS

▷ NOTES / IDEAS

THIS WEEK IN REVIEW

This Week's Big Wins

- [ ]
- [ ]
- [ ]
- [ ]
- [ ]
- [ ]
- [ ]
- [ ]

NOTES

NEXT WEEK AT A GLANCE

MON

TUE

WED

THU

FRI

SAT

SUN

DATE

| M | T | W | Th | F | Sa | Su |

▷ _____

▷ _____

▷ _____

To Do

- ☐ _____
- ☐ _____
- ☐ _____
- ☐ _____
- ☐ _____
- ☐ _____
- ☐ _____
- ☐ _____
- ☐ _____
- ☐ _____

Income Generating Activities

APPOINTMENTS

6am	
7am	
8am	
9am	
10am	
11am	
12pm	
1pm	
2pm	
3pm	
4pm	
5pm	
6pm	
7pm	

▷ AFFIRMATIONS

▷ SALES GOALS

▷ NOTES / IDEAS

| DATE | | M | T | W | Th | F | Sa | Su |

To Do

- ☐
- ☐
- ☐
- ☐
- ☐
- ☐
- ☐
- ☐
- ☐
- ☐

Income Generating Activities

APPOINTMENTS

6am
7am
8am
9am
10am
11am
12pm
1pm
2pm
3pm
4pm
5pm
6pm
7pm

AFFIRMATIONS

SALES GOALS

NOTES / IDEAS

DATE

M T W Th F Sa Su

TODAY'S TOP 3

To Do

- [ ]
- [ ]
- [ ]
- [ ]
- [ ]
- [ ]
- [ ]
- [ ]
- [ ]
- [ ]

Income Generating Activities

APPOINTMENTS

6am

7am

8am

9am

10am

11am

12pm

1pm

2pm

3pm

4pm

5pm

6pm

7pm

AFFIRMATIONS

SALES GOALS

NOTES / IDEAS

DATE

M   T   W   Th   F   Sa   Su

▷ ....

▷ ....

▷ ....

TODAY'S TOP 3

To Do

☐
☐
☐
☐
☐
☐
☐
☐
☐
☐

Income Generating Activities

APPOINTMENTS

6am
7am
8am
9am
10am
11am
12pm
1pm
2pm
3pm
4pm
5pm
6pm
7pm

▷ AFFIRMATIONS

▷ SALES GOALS

▷ NOTES / IDEAS

DATE　　　　　　　　　M　T　W　Th　F　Sa　Su

▷
▷
▷

TODAY'S TOP 3

To Do

☐
☐
☐
☐
☐
☐
☐
☐
☐
☐

Income Generating Activities

APPOINTMENTS

6am
7am
8am
9am
10am
11am
12pm
1pm
2pm
3pm
4pm
5pm
6pm
7pm

▷ AFFIRMATIONS

▷ SALES GOALS

▷ NOTES / IDEAS

DATE

M   T   W   Th   F   Sa   Su

▷

▷

▷

TODAY'S TOP 3

To Do

- ☐
- ☐
- ☐
- ☐
- ☐
- ☐
- ☐
- ☐
- ☐
- ☐

Income Generating Activities

APPOINTMENTS

6am

7am

8am

9am

10am

11am

12pm

1pm

2pm

3pm

4pm

5pm

6pm

7pm

▷ AFFIRMATIONS

▷ SALES GOALS

▷ NOTES / IDEAS

DATE

M T W Th F Sa Su

To Do

- [ ]
- [ ]
- [ ]
- [ ]
- [ ]
- [ ]
- [ ]
- [ ]
- [ ]
- [ ]
- [ ]

Income Generating Activities

APPOINTMENTS

6am
7am
8am
9am
10am
11am
12pm
1pm
2pm
3pm
4pm
5pm
6pm
7pm

AFFIRMATIONS

SALES GOALS

NOTES / IDEAS

THIS WEEK IN REVIEW

This Week's Big Wins

- [ ]
- [ ]
- [ ]
- [ ]
- [ ]
- [ ]
- [ ]

NOTES

NEXT WEEK AT A GLANCE

MON

TUE

WED

THU

FRI

SAT

SUN

_____ MONTH IN REVIEW

MONTHLY WINS

▷ _____   ▷ _____

▷ _____   ▷ _____

▷ _____   ▷ _____

▷ _____   ▷ _____

INCOME GENERATING HABITS THAT SUPPORT MONTHLY GOALS

▷ _____ ☐ DAILY HABIT ☐ WEEKLY HABIT

▷ _____ ☐ DAILY HABIT ☐ WEEKLY HABIT

▷ _____ ☐ DAILY HABIT ☐ WEEKLY HABIT

▷ _____ ☐ DAILY HABIT ☐ WEEKLY HABIT

▷ _____ ☐ DAILY HABIT ☐ WEEKLY HABIT

DAILY SALES

1. _____	11. _____	21. _____
2. _____	12. _____	22. _____
3. _____	13. _____	23. _____
4. _____	14. _____	24. _____
5. _____	15. _____	25. _____
6. _____	16. _____	26. _____
7. _____	17. _____	27. _____
8. _____	18. _____	28. _____
9. _____	19. _____	29. _____
10. _____	20. _____	30. _____

▷ *Make it happen.*

Remember Your Goals

MONTH _____

SUNDAY	MONDAY	TUESDAY	WEDNESDAY

Don't call it a dream – call it a plan.

THURSDAY	FRIDAY	SATURDAY

NOTES

_____
_____
_____
_____
_____
_____
_____
_____
_____
_____
_____
_____
_____
_____
_____
_____
_____
_____
_____
_____
_____
_____
_____
_____
_____
_____

DATE

M T W Th F Sa Su

TODAY'S TOP 3

To Do

- [ ]
- [ ]
- [ ]
- [ ]
- [ ]
- [ ]
- [ ]
- [ ]
- [ ]
- [ ]
- [ ]

Income Generating Activities

APPOINTMENTS

6am
7am
8am
9am
10am
11am
12pm
1pm
2pm
3pm
4pm
5pm
6pm
7pm

AFFIRMATIONS

SALES GOALS

NOTES / IDEAS

DATE

M   T   W   Th   F   Sa   Su

▷ _____

▷ _____

▷ _____

TODAY'S TOP 3

To Do

☐ _____
☐ _____
☐ _____
☐ _____
☐ _____
☐ _____
☐ _____
☐ _____
☐ _____
☐ _____

Income Generating Activities

_____
_____
_____
_____
_____
_____
_____
_____
_____
_____

APPOINTMENTS

6am _____

7am _____

8am _____

9am _____

10am _____

11am _____

12pm _____

1pm _____

2pm _____

3pm _____

4pm _____

5pm _____

6pm _____

7pm _____

▷ AFFIRMATIONS

▷ SALES GOALS

▷ NOTES / IDEAS

DATE

M   T   W   Th   F   Sa   Su

➤ _____

➤ _____

➤ _____

To Do

- ☐ _____
- ☐ _____
- ☐ _____
- ☐ _____
- ☐ _____
- ☐ _____
- ☐ _____
- ☐ _____
- ☐ _____
- ☐ _____

Income Generating Activities

APPOINTMENTS

6am	
7am	
8am	
9am	
10am	
11am	
12pm	
1pm	
2pm	
3pm	
4pm	
5pm	
6pm	
7pm	

➤ AFFIRMATIONS

➤ SALES GOALS

➤ NOTES / IDEAS

DATE

M   T   W   Th   F   Sa   Su

▶

▶

▶

TODAY'S TOP 3

To Do

- ☐
- ☐
- ☐
- ☐
- ☐
- ☐
- ☐
- ☐
- ☐
- ☐

Income Generating Activities

APPOINTMENTS

6am

7am

8am

9am

10am

11am

12pm

1pm

2pm

3pm

4pm

5pm

6pm

7pm

▶ AFFIRMATIONS

▶ SALES GOALS

▶ NOTES / IDEAS

DATE

M   T   W   Th   F   Sa   Su

▷

▷

▷

TODAY'S TOP 3

To Do

☐

☐

☐

☐

☐

☐

☐

☐

☐

☐

☐

Income Generating Activities

APPOINTMENTS

6am

7am

8am

9am

10am

11am

12pm

1pm

2pm

3pm

4pm

5pm

6pm

7pm

▷ AFFIRMATIONS

▷ SALES GOALS

▷ NOTES / IDEAS

DATE

M   T   W   Th   F   Sa   Su

▶ _____

▶ _____

▶ _____

TODAY'S TOP 3

To Do

- ☐ _____
- ☐ _____
- ☐ _____
- ☐ _____
- ☐ _____
- ☐ _____
- ☐ _____
- ☐ _____
- ☐ _____
- ☐ _____

Income Generating Activities

APPOINTMENTS

6am	
7am	
8am	
9am	
10am	
11am	
12pm	
1pm	
2pm	
3pm	
4pm	
5pm	
6pm	
7pm	

▶ AFFIRMATIONS

▶ SALES GOALS

▶ NOTES / IDEAS

DATE

M   T   W   Th   F   Sa   Su

TODAY'S TOP 3

▷ _____

▷ _____

▷ _____

To Do

- ☐ _____
- ☐ _____
- ☐ _____
- ☐ _____
- ☐ _____
- ☐ _____
- ☐ _____
- ☐ _____
- ☐ _____
- ☐ _____

Income Generating Activities

APPOINTMENTS

| 6am |
| 7am |
| 8am |
| 9am |
| 10am |
| 11am |
| 12pm |
| 1pm |
| 2pm |
| 3pm |
| 4pm |
| 5pm |
| 6pm |
| 7pm |

▷ AFFIRMATIONS

▷ SALES GOALS

▷ NOTES / IDEAS

THIS WEEK IN REVIEW

This Week's Big Wins

- [ ]
- [ ]
- [ ]
- [ ]
- [ ]
- [ ]
- [ ]

NOTES

NEXT WEEK AT A GLANCE

MON

TUE

WED

THU

FRI

SAT

SUN

DATE

M   T   W   Th   F   Sa   Su

▷ _____

▷ _____

▷ _____

To Do

☐ _____

☐ _____

☐ _____

☐ _____

☐ _____

☐ _____

☐ _____

☐ _____

☐ _____

☐ _____

☐ _____

Income Generating Activities

_____

_____

_____

_____

_____

_____

_____

_____

_____

_____

APPOINTMENTS

6am	
7am	
8am	
9am	
10am	
11am	
12pm	
1pm	
2pm	
3pm	
4pm	
5pm	
6pm	
7pm	

AFFIRMATIONS

SALES GOALS

NOTES / IDEAS

DATE

M   T   W   Th   F   Sa   Su

▶ _____

▶ _____

▶ _____

To Do

- ☐
- ☐
- ☐
- ☐
- ☐
- ☐
- ☐
- ☐
- ☐
- ☐

Income Generating Activities

APPOINTMENTS

6am

7am

8am

9am

10am

11am

12pm

1pm

2pm

3pm

4pm

5pm

6pm

7pm

▶ AFFIRMATIONS

▶ SALES GOALS

▶ NOTES / IDEAS

DATE

M   T   W   Th   F   Sa   Su

TODAY'S TOP 3

To Do

- [ ]
- [ ]
- [ ]
- [ ]
- [ ]
- [ ]
- [ ]
- [ ]
- [ ]
- [ ]

Income Generating Activities

APPOINTMENTS

6am
7am
8am
9am
10am
11am
12pm
1pm
2pm
3pm
4pm
5pm
6pm
7pm

AFFIRMATIONS

SALES GOALS

NOTES / IDEAS

DATE

M   T   W   Th   F   Sa   Su

TODAY'S TOP 3

▷ _____
▷ _____
▷ _____

To Do

☐ _____
☐ _____
☐ _____
☐ _____
☐ _____
☐ _____
☐ _____
☐ _____
☐ _____
☐ _____

Income Generating Activities

APPOINTMENTS

6am	
7am	
8am	
9am	
10am	
11am	
12pm	
1pm	
2pm	
3pm	
4pm	
5pm	
6pm	
7pm	

▷ AFFIRMATIONS

▷ SALES GOALS

▷ NOTES / IDEAS

DATE

M T W Th F Sa Su

▷
▷
▷

TODAY'S TOP 3

To Do

☐
☐
☐
☐
☐
☐
☐
☐
☐
☐

Income Generating Activities

APPOINTMENTS

6am
7am
8am
9am
10am
11am
12pm
1pm
2pm
3pm
4pm
5pm
6pm
7pm

▷ AFFIRMATIONS

▷ SALES GOALS

▷ NOTES / IDEAS

DATE

M   T   W   Th   F   Sa   Su

▷ ....

▷ ....

▷ ....

TODAY'S TOP 3

To Do

- ☐
- ☐
- ☐
- ☐
- ☐
- ☐
- ☐
- ☐
- ☐
- ☐

Income Generating Activities

APPOINTMENTS

6am

7am

8am

9am

10am

11am

12pm

1pm

2pm

3pm

4pm

5pm

6pm

7pm

▷ AFFIRMATIONS

▷ SALES GOALS

▷ NOTES / IDEAS

DATE

M T W Th F Sa Su

▷ ....

▷ ....

▷ ....

To Do

- ☐
- ☐
- ☐
- ☐
- ☐
- ☐
- ☐
- ☐
- ☐
- ☐

Income Generating Activities

APPOINTMENTS

6am

7am

8am

9am

10am

11am

12pm

1pm

2pm

3pm

4pm

5pm

6pm

7pm

▷ AFFIRMATIONS

▷ SALES GOALS

▷ NOTES / IDEAS

THIS WEEK IN REVIEW

This Week's Big Wins

☐ _____

☐ _____

☐ _____

☐ _____

☐ _____

☐ _____

☐ _____

☐ _____

NOTES

_____

_____

_____

_____

_____

_____

_____

NEXT WEEK AT A GLANCE

MON _____

TUE _____

WED _____

THU _____

FRI _____

SAT _____

SUN _____

DATE

M   T   W   Th   F   Sa   Su

▷
▷
▷

TODAY'S TOP 3

To Do

☐
☐
☐
☐
☐
☐
☐
☐
☐
☐
☐

Income Generating Activities

APPOINTMENTS

6am
7am
8am
9am
10am
11am
12pm
1pm
2pm
3pm
4pm
5pm
6pm
7pm

▷ AFFIRMATIONS

▷ SALES GOALS

▷ NOTES / IDEAS

DATE

M   T   W   Th   F   Sa   Su

TODAY'S TOP 3

To Do

- [ ]
- [ ]
- [ ]
- [ ]
- [ ]
- [ ]
- [ ]
- [ ]
- [ ]
- [ ]

Income Generating Activities

APPOINTMENTS

6am
7am
8am
9am
10am
11am
12pm
1pm
2pm
3pm
4pm
5pm
6pm
7pm

AFFIRMATIONS

SALES GOALS

NOTES / IDEAS

DATE

M   T   W   Th   F   Sa   Su

▷ _____

▷ _____

▷ _____

To Do

☐ _____

☐ _____

☐ _____

☐ _____

☐ _____

☐ _____

☐ _____

☐ _____

☐ _____

☐ _____

Income Generating Activities

_____

_____

_____

_____

_____

_____

_____

_____

_____

APPOINTMENTS

6am

7am

8am

9am

10am

11am

12pm

1pm

2pm

3pm

4pm

5pm

6pm

7pm

▷ AFFIRMATIONS

▷ SALES GOALS

▷ NOTES / IDEAS

DATE

M   T   W   Th   F   Sa   Su

TODAY'S TOP 3

▷
▷
▷

To Do

- ☐
- ☐
- ☐
- ☐
- ☐
- ☐
- ☐
- ☐
- ☐
- ☐

Income Generating Activities

APPOINTMENTS

6am
7am
8am
9am
10am
11am
12pm
1pm
2pm
3pm
4pm
5pm
6pm
7pm

▷ AFFIRMATIONS

▷ SALES GOALS

▷ NOTES / IDEAS

DATE

M   T   W   Th   F   Sa   Su

▷ _____

▷ _____

▷ _____

TODAY'S TOP 3

To Do

- ☐ _____
- ☐ _____
- ☐ _____
- ☐ _____
- ☐ _____
- ☐ _____
- ☐ _____
- ☐ _____
- ☐ _____
- ☐ _____
- ☐ _____

Income Generating Activities

APPOINTMENTS

6am	
7am	▷ **AFFIRMATIONS**
8am	
9am	
10am	
11am	▷ **SALES GOALS**
12pm	
1pm	
2pm	
3pm	
4pm	▷ **NOTES / IDEAS**
5pm	
6pm	
7pm	

DATE

M T W Th F Sa Su

TODAY'S TOP 3

▷

▷

▷

To Do

☐

☐

☐

☐

☐

☐

☐

☐

☐

☐

Income Generating Activities

APPOINTMENTS

6am

7am

8am

9am

10am

11am

12pm

1pm

2pm

3pm

4pm

5pm

6pm

7pm

▷ AFFIRMATIONS

▷ SALES GOALS

▷ NOTES / IDEAS

DATE

M   T   W   Th   F   Sa   Su

▶ _____

▶ _____

▶ _____

TODAY'S TOP 3

To Do

☐ _____

☐ _____

☐ _____

☐ _____

☐ _____

☐ _____

☐ _____

☐ _____

☐ _____

☐ _____

Income Generating Activities

APPOINTMENTS

6am

7am

8am

9am

10am

11am

12pm

1pm

2pm

3pm

4pm

5pm

6pm

7pm

▶ AFFIRMATIONS

▶ SALES GOALS

▶ NOTES / IDEAS

THIS WEEK IN REVIEW

This Week's Big Wins

- [ ] _____
- [ ] _____
- [ ] _____
- [ ] _____
- [ ] _____
- [ ] _____
- [ ] _____
- [ ] _____

NOTES

_____

_____

_____

_____

_____

_____

_____

_____

NEXT WEEK AT A GLANCE

MON

TUE

WED

THU

FRI

SAT

SUN

To Do

- ☐
- ☐
- ☐
- ☐
- ☐
- ☐
- ☐
- ☐
- ☐
- ☐
- ☐

Income Generating Activities

APPOINTMENTS

6am

7am

8am

9am

10am

11am

12pm

1pm

2pm

3pm

4pm

5pm

6pm

7pm

AFFIRMATIONS

SALES GOALS

NOTES / IDEAS

DATE

M   T   W   Th   F   Sa   Su

▷ _____

▷ _____

▷ _____

TODAY'S TOP 3

To Do

- ☐ _____
- ☐ _____
- ☐ _____
- ☐ _____
- ☐ _____
- ☐ _____
- ☐ _____
- ☐ _____
- ☐ _____
- ☐ _____
- ☐ _____

Income Generating Activities

APPOINTMENTS

6am _____

7am _____

8am _____

9am _____

10am _____

11am _____

12pm _____

1pm _____

2pm _____

3pm _____

4pm _____

5pm _____

6pm _____

7pm _____

▷ AFFIRMATIONS

▷ SALES GOALS

▷ NOTES / IDEAS

DATE

M   T   W   Th   F   Sa   Su

▷

▷

▷

To Do

- ☐
- ☐
- ☐
- ☐
- ☐
- ☐
- ☐
- ☐
- ☐
- ☐
- ☐

Income Generating Activities

APPOINTMENTS

6am	
7am	▷ **AFFIRMATIONS**
8am	
9am	
10am	
11am	▷ **SALES GOALS**
12pm	
1pm	
2pm	
3pm	
4pm	▷ **NOTES / IDEAS**
5pm	
6pm	
7pm	

DATE

M   T   W   Th   F   Sa   Su

▷ _____

▷ _____

▷ _____

TODAY'S TOP 3

To Do

- ☐
- ☐
- ☐
- ☐
- ☐
- ☐
- ☐
- ☐
- ☐
- ☐

Income Generating Activities

APPOINTMENTS

6am	
7am	
8am	
9am	
10am	
11am	
12pm	
1pm	
2pm	
3pm	
4pm	
5pm	
6pm	
7pm	

▷ AFFIRMATIONS

▷ SALES GOALS

▷ NOTES / IDEAS

DATE

M   T   W   Th   F   Sa   Su

▷ _____

▷ _____

▷ _____

To Do

- ☐ _____
- ☐ _____
- ☐ _____
- ☐ _____
- ☐ _____
- ☐ _____
- ☐ _____
- ☐ _____
- ☐ _____
- ☐ _____
- ☐ _____

Income Generating Activities

APPOINTMENTS

6am _____

7am _____

8am _____

9am _____

10am _____

11am _____

12pm _____

1pm _____

2pm _____

3pm _____

4pm _____

5pm _____

6pm _____

7pm _____

▷ AFFIRMATIONS

▷ SALES GOALS

▷ NOTES / IDEAS

DATE

M   T   W   Th   F   Sa   Su

TODAY'S TOP 3

To Do

- [ ]
- [ ]
- [ ]
- [ ]
- [ ]
- [ ]
- [ ]
- [ ]
- [ ]
- [ ]
- [ ]

Income Generating Activities

APPOINTMENTS

6am

7am

8am

9am

10am

11am

12pm

1pm

2pm

3pm

4pm

5pm

6pm

7pm

AFFIRMATIONS

SALES GOALS

NOTES / IDEAS

DATE

≫
≫
≫

TODAY'S TOP 3

To Do

☐
☐
☐
☐
☐
☐
☐
☐
☐
☐

Income Generating Activities

APPOINTMENTS

6am
7am
8am
9am
10am
11am
12pm
1pm
2pm
3pm
4pm
5pm
6pm
7pm

≫ AFFIRMATIONS

≫ SALES GOALS

≫ NOTES / IDEAS

THIS WEEK IN REVIEW

This Week's Big Wins

- ☐
- ☐
- ☐
- ☐
- ☐
- ☐
- ☐
- ☐

NOTES

NEXT WEEK AT A GLANCE

MON

TUE

WED

THU

FRI

SAT

SUN

DATE

M   T   W   Th   F   Sa   Su

TODAY'S TOP 3

To Do

- ☐
- ☐
- ☐
- ☐
- ☐
- ☐
- ☐
- ☐
- ☐
- ☐
- ☐

Income Generating Activities

APPOINTMENTS

6am

7am

8am

9am

10am

11am

12pm

1pm

2pm

3pm

4pm

5pm

6pm

7pm

AFFIRMATIONS

SALES GOALS

NOTES / IDEAS

DATE

M   T   W   Th   F   Sa   Su

▷ ....

▷ ....

▷ ....

TODAY'S TOP 3

To Do

☐ ....
☐ ....
☐ ....
☐ ....
☐ ....
☐ ....
☐ ....
☐ ....
☐ ....
☐ ....
☐ ....

Income Generating Activities

APPOINTMENTS

6am ....
7am ....
8am ....
9am ....
10am ....
11am ....
12pm ....
1pm ....
2pm ....
3pm ....
4pm ....
5pm ....
6pm ....
7pm ....

▷ AFFIRMATIONS

▷ SALES GOALS

▷ NOTES / IDEAS

DATE   M   T   W   Th   F   Sa   Su

▷ _____

▷ _____

▷ _____

TODAY'S TOP 3

To Do

- ☐ _____
- ☐ _____
- ☐ _____
- ☐ _____
- ☐ _____
- ☐ _____
- ☐ _____
- ☐ _____
- ☐ _____
- ☐ _____
- ☐ _____

Income Generating Activities

APPOINTMENTS

6am
7am
8am
9am
10am
11am
12pm
1pm
2pm
3pm
4pm
5pm
6pm
7pm

▷ AFFIRMATIONS

▷ SALES GOALS

▷ NOTES / IDEAS

DATE

M   T   W   Th   F   Sa   Su

▷

▷

▷

TODAY'S TOP 3

To Do

- ☐
- ☐
- ☐
- ☐
- ☐
- ☐
- ☐
- ☐
- ☐
- ☐

Income Generating Activities

APPOINTMENTS

6am	
7am	
8am	
9am	
10am	
11am	
12pm	
1pm	
2pm	
3pm	
4pm	
5pm	
6pm	
7pm	

▷ AFFIRMATIONS

▷ SALES GOALS

▷ NOTES / IDEAS

DATE

M T W Th F Sa Su

To Do

- [ ]
- [ ]
- [ ]
- [ ]
- [ ]
- [ ]
- [ ]
- [ ]
- [ ]
- [ ]
- [ ]

Income Generating Activities

APPOINTMENTS

6am
7am
8am
9am
10am
11am
12pm
1pm
2pm
3pm
4pm
5pm
6pm
7pm

AFFIRMATIONS

SALES GOALS

NOTES / IDEAS

DATE   M   T   W   Th   F   Sa   Su

TODAY'S TOP 3

To Do

- [ ]
- [ ]
- [ ]
- [ ]
- [ ]
- [ ]
- [ ]
- [ ]
- [ ]
- [ ]

Income Generating Activities

APPOINTMENTS

6am	
7am	
8am	
9am	
10am	
11am	
12pm	
1pm	
2pm	
3pm	
4pm	
5pm	
6pm	
7pm	

AFFIRMATIONS

SALES GOALS

NOTES / IDEAS

DATE

M   T   W   Th   F   Sa   Su

▷ _____

▷ _____

▷ _____

TODAY'S TOP 3

To Do

- ☐ _____
- ☐ _____
- ☐ _____
- ☐ _____
- ☐ _____
- ☐ _____
- ☐ _____
- ☐ _____
- ☐ _____
- ☐ _____
- ☐ _____

Income Generating Activities

APPOINTMENTS

6am

7am

8am

9am

10am

11am

12pm

1pm

2pm

3pm

4pm

5pm

6pm

7pm

▷ AFFIRMATIONS

▷ SALES GOALS

▷ NOTES / IDEAS

THIS WEEK IN REVIEW

This Week's Big Wins

- [ ] _____
- [ ] _____
- [ ] _____
- [ ] _____
- [ ] _____
- [ ] _____
- [ ] _____

NOTES

_____

_____

_____

_____

_____

_____

_____

_____

NEXT WEEK AT A GLANCE

MON _____

TUE _____

WED _____

THU _____

FRI _____

SAT _____

SUN _____

_____ MONTH IN REVIEW

MONTHLY WINS

▷
▷
▷
▷

▷
▷
▷
▷

INCOME GENERATING HABITS THAT SUPPORT MONTHLY GOALS

▷ ☐ DAILY HABIT ☐ WEEKLY HABIT

▷ ☐ DAILY HABIT ☐ WEEKLY HABIT

▷ ☐ DAILY HABIT ☐ WEEKLY HABIT

▷ ☐ DAILY HABIT ☐ WEEKLY HABIT

▷ ☐ DAILY HABIT ☐ WEEKLY HABIT

DAILY SALES

1.	11.	21.
2.	12.	22.
3.	13.	23.
4.	14.	24.
5.	15.	25.
6.	16.	26.
7.	17.	27.
8.	18.	28.
9.	19.	29.
10.	20.	30.

▷ _Everything you do now is for your future._

Dream Big

MONTH _____

SUNDAY	MONDAY	TUESDAY	WEDNESDAY

Trust the timing of your life.

THURSDAY	FRIDAY	SATURDAY	NOTES

DATE

M T W Th F Sa Su

To Do

- [ ]
- [ ]
- [ ]
- [ ]
- [ ]
- [ ]
- [ ]
- [ ]
- [ ]
- [ ]

Income Generating Activities

APPOINTMENTS

6am
7am
8am
9am
10am
11am
12pm
1pm
2pm
3pm
4pm
5pm
6pm
7pm

AFFIRMATIONS

SALES GOALS

NOTES / IDEAS

DATE

M   T   W   Th   F   Sa   Su

➤

➤

➤

TODAY'S TOP 3

To Do

- ☐
- ☐
- ☐
- ☐
- ☐
- ☐
- ☐
- ☐
- ☐
- ☐

Income Generating Activities

APPOINTMENTS

6am

7am

8am

9am

10am

11am

12pm

1pm

2pm

3pm

4pm

5pm

6pm

7pm

➤ AFFIRMATIONS

➤ SALES GOALS

➤ NOTES / IDEAS

DATE

M   T   W   Th   F   Sa   Su

▷ _____

▷ _____

▷ _____

TODAY'S TOP 3

To Do

☐ _____

☐ _____

☐ _____

☐ _____

☐ _____

☐ _____

☐ _____

☐ _____

☐ _____

☐ _____

Income Generating Activities

APPOINTMENTS

6am

7am

8am

9am

10am

11am

12pm

1pm

2pm

3pm

4pm

5pm

6pm

7pm

▷ AFFIRMATIONS

▷ SALES GOALS

▷ NOTES / IDEAS

DATE

M   T   W   Th   F   Sa   Su

TODAY'S TOP 3

To Do

- ☐
- ☐
- ☐
- ☐
- ☐
- ☐
- ☐
- ☐
- ☐
- ☐

Income Generating Activities

APPOINTMENTS

6am	
7am	
8am	
9am	
10am	
11am	
12pm	
1pm	
2pm	
3pm	
4pm	
5pm	
6pm	
7pm	

AFFIRMATIONS

SALES GOALS

NOTES / IDEAS

DATE			M	T	W	Th	F	Sa	Su

▷
▷
▷

To Do

☐
☐
☐
☐
☐
☐
☐
☐
☐
☐

Income Generating Activities

APPOINTMENTS

6am
7am
8am
9am
10am
11am
12pm
1pm
2pm
3pm
4pm
5pm
6pm
7pm

▷ AFFIRMATIONS

▷ SALES GOALS

▷ NOTES / IDEAS

DATE

M   T   W   Th   F   Sa   Su

▷

▷

▷

TODAY'S TOP 3

To Do

- ☐
- ☐
- ☐
- ☐
- ☐
- ☐
- ☐
- ☐
- ☐
- ☐

Income Generating Activities

APPOINTMENTS

6am	
7am	
8am	
9am	
10am	
11am	
12pm	
1pm	
2pm	
3pm	
4pm	
5pm	
6pm	
7pm	

▷ AFFIRMATIONS

▷ SALES GOALS

▷ NOTES / IDEAS

DATE

M T W Th F Sa Su

▷
▷
▷

To Do

- ☐
- ☐
- ☐
- ☐
- ☐
- ☐
- ☐
- ☐
- ☐
- ☐
- ☐

Income Generating Activities

APPOINTMENTS

6am
7am
8am
9am
10am
11am
12pm
1pm
2pm
3pm
4pm
5pm
6pm
7pm

▷ AFFIRMATIONS

▷ SALES GOALS

▷ NOTES / IDEAS

THIS WEEK IN REVIEW

This Week's Big Wins

☐ _____

☐ _____

☐ _____

☐ _____

☐ _____

☐ _____

☐ _____

NOTES

_____

_____

_____

_____

_____

NEXT WEEK AT A GLANCE

MON

TUE

WED

THU

FRI

SAT

SUN

DATE

M T W Th F Sa Su

▷
▷
▷

To Do

- ☐
- ☐
- ☐
- ☐
- ☐
- ☐
- ☐
- ☐
- ☐
- ☐
- ☐

Income Generating Activities

APPOINTMENTS

6am	
7am	
8am	
9am	
10am	
11am	
12pm	
1pm	
2pm	
3pm	
4pm	
5pm	
6pm	
7pm	

▷ AFFIRMATIONS

▷ SALES GOALS

▷ NOTES / IDEAS

DATE

M T W Th F Sa Su

TODAY'S TOP 3

▷ _____

▷ _____

▷ _____

To Do

☐ _____

☐ _____

☐ _____

☐ _____

☐ _____

☐ _____

☐ _____

☐ _____

☐ _____

☐ _____

Income Generating Activities

APPOINTMENTS

6am
7am
8am
9am
10am
11am
12pm
1pm
2pm
3pm
4pm
5pm
6pm
7pm

▷ AFFIRMATIONS

▷ SALES GOALS

▷ NOTES / IDEAS

DATE

M T W Th F Sa Su

▷
▷
▷

To Do

- [ ]
- [ ]
- [ ]
- [ ]
- [ ]
- [ ]
- [ ]
- [ ]
- [ ]
- [ ]
- [ ]

Income Generating Activities

APPOINTMENTS

6am
7am
8am
9am
10am
11am
12pm
1pm
2pm
3pm
4pm
5pm
6pm
7pm

▷ AFFIRMATIONS

▷ SALES GOALS

▷ NOTES / IDEAS

DATE

M   T   W   Th   F   Sa   Su

▷ ....

▷ ....

▷ ....

TODAY'S TOP 3

To Do

☐ ....

☐ ....

☐ ....

☐ ....

☐ ....

☐ ....

☐ ....

☐ ....

☐ ....

☐ ....

☐ ....

Income Generating Activities

APPOINTMENTS

6am ....

7am ....

8am ....

9am ....

10am ....

11am ....

12pm ....

1pm ....

2pm ....

3pm ....

4pm ....

5pm ....

6pm ....

7pm ....

▷ AFFIRMATIONS

▷ SALES GOALS

▷ NOTES / IDEAS

DATE

M T W Th F Sa Su

▷ _____

▷ _____

▷ _____

TODAY'S TOP 3

To Do

☐ _____

☐ _____

☐ _____

☐ _____

☐ _____

☐ _____

☐ _____

☐ _____

☐ _____

☐ _____

Income Generating Activities

APPOINTMENTS

6am

7am

8am

9am

10am

11am

12pm

1pm

2pm

3pm

4pm

5pm

6pm

7pm

▷ AFFIRMATIONS

▷ SALES GOALS

▷ NOTES / IDEAS

DATE

M   T   W   Th   F   Sa   Su

▶

▶

▶

TODAY'S TOP 3

To Do

- ☐
- ☐
- ☐
- ☐
- ☐
- ☐
- ☐
- ☐
- ☐
- ☐

Income Generating Activities

APPOINTMENTS

6am

7am

8am

9am

10am

11am

12pm

1pm

2pm

3pm

4pm

5pm

6pm

7pm

▶ AFFIRMATIONS

▶ SALES GOALS

▶ NOTES / IDEAS

DATE

M T W Th F Sa Su

▶
▶
▶

TODAY'S TOP 3

To Do

- ☐
- ☐
- ☐
- ☐
- ☐
- ☐
- ☐
- ☐
- ☐
- ☐

Income Generating Activities

APPOINTMENTS

6am
7am
8am
9am
10am
11am
12pm
1pm
2pm
3pm
4pm
5pm
6pm
7pm

▶ AFFIRMATIONS

▶ SALES GOALS

▶ NOTES / IDEAS

THIS WEEK IN REVIEW

This Week's Big Wins

☐ _____

☐ _____

☐ _____

☐ _____

☐ _____

☐ _____

☐ _____

☐ _____

NOTES

_____

_____

_____

_____

_____

_____

_____

_____

NEXT WEEK AT A GLANCE

MON _____

TUE _____

WED _____

THU _____

FRI _____

SAT _____

SUN _____

DATE

M   T   W   Th   F   Sa   Su

▷
▷
▷

To Do

☐
☐
☐
☐
☐
☐
☐
☐
☐
☐

Income Generating Activities

APPOINTMENTS

6am
7am
8am
9am
10am
11am
12pm
1pm
2pm
3pm
4pm
5pm
6pm
7pm

▷ AFFIRMATIONS

▷ SALES GOALS

▷ NOTES / IDEAS

DATE

M   T   W   Th   F   Sa   Su

▷ _____

▷ _____

▷ _____

TODAY'S TOP 3

To Do

- ☐ _____
- ☐ _____
- ☐ _____
- ☐ _____
- ☐ _____
- ☐ _____
- ☐ _____
- ☐ _____
- ☐ _____
- ☐ _____
- ☐ _____

Income Generating Activities

APPOINTMENTS

6am	
7am	
8am	
9am	
10am	
11am	
12pm	
1pm	
2pm	
3pm	
4pm	
5pm	
6pm	
7pm	

▷ AFFIRMATIONS

▷ SALES GOALS

▷ NOTES / IDEAS

DATE

M   T   W   Th   F   Sa   Su

▷ ....

▷ ....

▷ ....

To Do

☐ ....

☐ ....

☐ ....

☐ ....

☐ ....

☐ ....

☐ ....

☐ ....

☐ ....

☐ ....

☐ ....

Income Generating Activities

APPOINTMENTS

6am	
7am	
8am	
9am	
10am	
11am	
12pm	
1pm	
2pm	
3pm	
4pm	
5pm	
6pm	
7pm	

▷ AFFIRMATIONS

▷ SALES GOALS

▷ NOTES / IDEAS

DATE

M T W Th F Sa Su

▷ ....

▷ ....

▷ ....

To Do

☐ ....

☐ ....

☐ ....

☐ ....

☐ ....

☐ ....

☐ ....

☐ ....

☐ ....

☐ ....

Income Generating Activities

APPOINTMENTS

6am	
7am	
8am	
9am	
10am	
11am	
12pm	
1pm	
2pm	
3pm	
4pm	
5pm	
6pm	
7pm	

▷ AFFIRMATIONS

▷ SALES GOALS

▷ NOTES / IDEAS

DATE

M   T   W   Th   F   Sa   Su

▷
▷
▷

TODAY'S TOP 3

To Do

- ☐
- ☐
- ☐
- ☐
- ☐
- ☐
- ☐
- ☐
- ☐
- ☐

Income Generating Activities

APPOINTMENTS

6am
7am
8am
9am
10am
11am
12pm
1pm
2pm
3pm
4pm
5pm
6pm
7pm

▷ AFFIRMATIONS

▷ SALES GOALS

▷ NOTES / IDEAS

DATE

M   T   W   Th   F   Sa   Su

▷ ....

▷ ....

▷ ....

TODAY'S TOP 3

To Do

- ☐
- ☐
- ☐
- ☐
- ☐
- ☐
- ☐
- ☐
- ☐
- ☐

Income Generating Activities

APPOINTMENTS

6am
7am
8am
9am
10am
11am
12pm
1pm
2pm
3pm
4pm
5pm
6pm
7pm

▷ AFFIRMATIONS

▷ SALES GOALS

▷ NOTES / IDEAS

DATE

M T W Th F Sa Su

▷
▷
▷

TODAY'S TOP 3

To Do

☐
☐
☐
☐
☐
☐
☐
☐
☐
☐

Income Generating Activities

APPOINTMENTS

6am
7am
8am
9am
10am
11am
12pm
1pm
2pm
3pm
4pm
5pm
6pm
7pm

▷ AFFIRMATIONS

▷ SALES GOALS

▷ NOTES / IDEAS

THIS WEEK IN REVIEW

This Week's Big Wins

- [ ]
- [ ]
- [ ]
- [ ]
- [ ]
- [ ]
- [ ]

NOTES

NEXT WEEK AT A GLANCE

MON

TUE

WED

THU

FRI

SAT

SUN

DATE

M   T   W   Th   F   Sa   Su

▷

▷

▷

TODAY'S TOP 3

To Do

- ☐
- ☐
- ☐
- ☐
- ☐
- ☐
- ☐
- ☐
- ☐
- ☐
- ☐

Income Generating Activities

APPOINTMENTS

6am	
7am	
8am	
9am	
10am	
11am	
12pm	
1pm	
2pm	
3pm	
4pm	
5pm	
6pm	
7pm	

▷ AFFIRMATIONS

▷ SALES GOALS

▷ NOTES / IDEAS

DATE		M	T	W	Th	F	Sa	Su

TODAY'S TOP 3

To Do

- [ ]
- [ ]
- [ ]
- [ ]
- [ ]
- [ ]
- [ ]
- [ ]
- [ ]
- [ ]
- [ ]

Income Generating Activities

APPOINTMENTS

6am
7am
8am
9am
10am
11am
12pm
1pm
2pm
3pm
4pm
5pm
6pm
7pm

AFFIRMATIONS

SALES GOALS

NOTES / IDEAS

DATE

	M	T	W	Th	F	Sa	Su

▷

▷

▷

TODAY'S TOP 3

To Do

☐

☐

☐

☐

☐

☐

☐

☐

☐

☐

Income Generating Activities

APPOINTMENTS

6am

7am

8am

9am

10am

11am

12pm

1pm

2pm

3pm

4pm

5pm

6pm

7pm

▷ AFFIRMATIONS

▷ SALES GOALS

▷ NOTES / IDEAS

DATE

M T W Th F Sa Su

TODAY'S TOP 3

To Do

- [ ]
- [ ]
- [ ]
- [ ]
- [ ]
- [ ]
- [ ]
- [ ]
- [ ]
- [ ]

Income Generating Activities

APPOINTMENTS

6am

7am

8am

9am

10am

11am

12pm

1pm

2pm

3pm

4pm

5pm

6pm

7pm

AFFIRMATIONS

SALES GOALS

NOTES / IDEAS

▷ _____

▷ _____

▷ _____

To Do

☐ _____

☐ _____

☐ _____

☐ _____

☐ _____

☐ _____

☐ _____

☐ _____

☐ _____

☐ _____

☐ _____

Income Generating Activities

APPOINTMENTS

6am

7am

8am

9am

10am

11am

12pm

1pm

2pm

3pm

4pm

5pm

6pm

7pm

▷ AFFIRMATIONS

▷ SALES GOALS

▷ NOTES / IDEAS

DATE

M   T   W   Th   F   Sa   Su

▷ ....

▷ ....

▷ ....

TODAY'S TOP 3

To Do

- ☐
- ☐
- ☐
- ☐
- ☐
- ☐
- ☐
- ☐
- ☐
- ☐

Income Generating Activities

APPOINTMENTS

6am

7am

8am

9am

10am

11am

12pm

1pm

2pm

3pm

4pm

5pm

6pm

7pm

▷ AFFIRMATIONS

▷ SALES GOALS

▷ NOTES / IDEAS

DATE

M T W Th F Sa Su

▷

▷

▷

To Do

- ☐
- ☐
- ☐
- ☐
- ☐
- ☐
- ☐
- ☐
- ☐
- ☐
- ☐

Income Generating Activities

APPOINTMENTS

6am	
7am	
8am	
9am	
10am	
11am	
12pm	
1pm	
2pm	
3pm	
4pm	
5pm	
6pm	
7pm	

▷ AFFIRMATIONS

▷ SALES GOALS

▷ NOTES / IDEAS

THIS WEEK IN REVIEW

This Week's Big Wins

☐ _____

☐ _____

☐ _____

☐ _____

☐ _____

☐ _____

☐ _____

NOTES

_____

_____

_____

_____

_____

_____

_____

_____

NEXT WEEK AT A GLANCE

MON _____

TUE _____

WED _____

THU _____

FRI _____

SAT _____

SUN _____

DATE

M   T   W   Th   F   Sa   Su

▷
▷
▷

To Do

☐
☐
☐
☐
☐
☐
☐
☐
☐
☐

Income Generating Activities

APPOINTMENTS

6am
7am
8am
9am
10am
11am
12pm
1pm
2pm
3pm
4pm
5pm
6pm
7pm

▷ AFFIRMATIONS

▷ SALES GOALS

▷ NOTES / IDEAS

DATE

M T W Th F Sa Su

TODAY'S TOP 3

To Do

- [ ]
- [ ]
- [ ]
- [ ]
- [ ]
- [ ]
- [ ]
- [ ]
- [ ]
- [ ]
- [ ]

Income Generating Activities

APPOINTMENTS

6am
7am
8am
9am
10am
11am
12pm
1pm
2pm
3pm
4pm
5pm
6pm
7pm

AFFIRMATIONS

SALES GOALS

NOTES / IDEAS

DATE

M T W Th F Sa Su

▷ _____

▷ _____

▷ _____

TODAY'S TOP 3

To Do

- ☐ _____
- ☐ _____
- ☐ _____
- ☐ _____
- ☐ _____
- ☐ _____
- ☐ _____
- ☐ _____
- ☐ _____
- ☐ _____
- ☐ _____

Income Generating Activities

APPOINTMENTS

6am	
7am	
8am	
9am	
10am	
11am	
12pm	
1pm	
2pm	
3pm	
4pm	
5pm	
6pm	
7pm	

▷ AFFIRMATIONS

▷ SALES GOALS

▷ NOTES / IDEAS

DATE		M	T	W	Th	F	Sa	Su

▷ _____

▷ _____

▷ _____

TODAY'S TOP 3

To Do

☐
☐
☐
☐
☐
☐
☐
☐
☐
☐

Income Generating Activities

APPOINTMENTS

6am
7am
8am
9am
10am
11am
12pm
1pm
2pm
3pm
4pm
5pm
6pm
7pm

▷ AFFIRMATIONS

▷ SALES GOALS

▷ NOTES / IDEAS

▷ ....

▷ ....

▷ ....

TODAY'S TOP 3

To Do

☐ ....

☐ ....

☐ ....

☐ ....

☐ ....

☐ ....

☐ ....

☐ ....

☐ ....

☐ ....

☐ ....

Income Generating Activities

APPOINTMENTS

6am	
7am	
8am	
9am	
10am	
11am	
12pm	
1pm	
2pm	
3pm	
4pm	
5pm	
6pm	
7pm	

▷ AFFIRMATIONS

▷ SALES GOALS

▷ NOTES / IDEAS

DATE		M	T	W	Th	F	Sa	Su

TODAY'S TOP 3

▷ _____

▷ _____

▷ _____

To Do

☐ _____
☐ _____
☐ _____
☐ _____
☐ _____
☐ _____
☐ _____
☐ _____
☐ _____
☐ _____

Income Generating Activities

APPOINTMENTS

6am	
7am	
8am	
9am	
10am	
11am	
12pm	
1pm	
2pm	
3pm	
4pm	
5pm	
6pm	
7pm	

▷ AFFIRMATIONS

▷ SALES GOALS

▷ NOTES / IDEAS

DATE

M	T	W	Th	F	Sa	Su

▷

▷

▷

To Do

☐

☐

☐

☐

☐

☐

☐

☐

☐

☐

Income Generating Activities

APPOINTMENTS

6am

7am

8am

9am

10am

11am

12pm

1pm

2pm

3pm

4pm

5pm

6pm

7pm

▷ AFFIRMATIONS

▷ SALES GOALS

▷ NOTES / IDEAS

THIS WEEK IN REVIEW

This Week's Big Wins

☐ _____

☐ _____

☐ _____

☐ _____

☐ _____

☐ _____

☐ _____

☐ _____

NOTES

_____

_____

_____

_____

_____

_____

_____

NEXT WEEK AT A GLANCE

MON

TUE

WED

THU

FRI

SAT

SUN

_____ MONTH IN REVIEW

MONTHLY WINS

▷

▷

▷

▷

▷

▷

▷

▷

INCOME GENERATING HABITS THAT SUPPORT MONTHLY GOALS

▷ ☐ DAILY HABIT   ☐ WEEKLY HABIT

▷ ☐ DAILY HABIT   ☐ WEEKLY HABIT

▷ ☐ DAILY HABIT   ☐ WEEKLY HABIT

▷ ☐ DAILY HABIT   ☐ WEEKLY HABIT

▷ ☐ DAILY HABIT   ☐ WEEKLY HABIT

DAILY SALES

1.	11.	21.
2.	12.	22.
3.	13.	23.
4.	14.	24.
5.	15.	25.
6.	16.	26.
7.	17.	27.
8.	18.	28.
9.	19.	29.
10.	20.	30.

▷ *If you can dream it, you can do it.*

You Define Success

MONTH _____

SUNDAY	MONDAY	TUESDAY	WEDNESDAY

Every day is a new beginning.

THURSDAY	FRIDAY	SATURDAY	NOTES

DATE

M   T   W   Th   F   Sa   Su

▷ _____

▷ _____

▷ _____

TODAY'S TOP 3

To Do

☐ _____
☐ _____
☐ _____
☐ _____
☐ _____
☐ _____
☐ _____
☐ _____
☐ _____
☐ _____
☐ _____

Income Generating Activities

APPOINTMENTS

6am
7am
8am
9am
10am
11am

▷ AFFIRMATIONS

▷ SALES GOALS

12pm
1pm
2pm
3pm
4pm

▷ NOTES / IDEAS

5pm
6pm
7pm

DATE

M   T   W   Th   F   Sa   Su

▷

▷

▷

TODAY'S TOP 3

To Do

- [ ]
- [ ]
- [ ]
- [ ]
- [ ]
- [ ]
- [ ]
- [ ]
- [ ]

Income Generating Activities

APPOINTMENTS

6am

7am

8am

9am

10am

11am

12pm

1pm

2pm

3pm

4pm

5pm

6pm

7pm

▷ AFFIRMATIONS

▷ SALES GOALS

▷ NOTES / IDEAS

DATE

M   T   W   Th   F   Sa   Su

▷

▷

▷

TODAY'S TOP 3

To Do

☐

☐

☐

☐

☐

☐

☐

☐

☐

☐

Income Generating Activities

APPOINTMENTS

6am

7am

8am

9am

10am

11am

12pm

1pm

2pm

3pm

4pm

5pm

6pm

7pm

▷ AFFIRMATIONS

▷ SALES GOALS

▷ NOTES / IDEAS

DATE

M T W Th F Sa Su

>
>
>

TODAY'S TOP 3

To Do

- [ ]
- [ ]
- [ ]
- [ ]
- [ ]
- [ ]
- [ ]
- [ ]
- [ ]
- [ ]
- [ ]

Income Generating Activities

APPOINTMENTS

6am
7am
8am
9am
10am
11am
12pm
1pm
2pm
3pm
4pm
5pm
6pm
7pm

> AFFIRMATIONS

> SALES GOALS

> NOTES / IDEAS

DATE

M   T   W   Th   F   Sa   Su

▷ _____

▷ _____

▷ _____

TODAY'S TOP 3

To Do

- ☐ _____
- ☐ _____
- ☐ _____
- ☐ _____
- ☐ _____
- ☐ _____
- ☐ _____
- ☐ _____
- ☐ _____
- ☐ _____
- ☐ _____

Income Generating Activities

_____

_____

_____

_____

_____

_____

_____

_____

_____

APPOINTMENTS

6am

7am

8am

9am

10am

11am

12pm

1pm

2pm

3pm

4pm

5pm

6pm

7pm

▷ AFFIRMATIONS

▷ SALES GOALS

▷ NOTES / IDEAS

DATE

M   T   W   Th   F   Sa   Su

▷ _____

▷ _____

▷ _____

To Do

☐ _____

☐ _____

☐ _____

☐ _____

☐ _____

☐ _____

☐ _____

☐ _____

☐ _____

☐ _____

Income Generating Activities

APPOINTMENTS

6am _____

7am _____

8am _____

9am _____

10am _____

11am _____

12pm _____

1pm _____

2pm _____

3pm _____

4pm _____

5pm _____

6pm _____

7pm _____

▷ **AFFIRMATIONS**

▷ **SALES GOALS**

▷ **NOTES / IDEAS**

DATE

M T W Th F Sa Su

TODAY'S TOP 3

▶ _____
▶ _____
▶ _____

To Do

- [ ] _____
- [ ] _____
- [ ] _____
- [ ] _____
- [ ] _____
- [ ] _____
- [ ] _____
- [ ] _____
- [ ] _____
- [ ] _____

Income Generating Activities

APPOINTMENTS

6am	
7am	
8am	
9am	
10am	
11am	
12pm	
1pm	
2pm	
3pm	
4pm	
5pm	
6pm	
7pm	

▶ AFFIRMATIONS

▶ SALES GOALS

▶ NOTES / IDEAS

THIS WEEK IN REVIEW

This Week's Big Wins

☐ _____

☐ _____

☐ _____

☐ _____

☐ _____

☐ _____

☐ _____

☐ _____

NOTES

_____

_____

_____

_____

_____

_____

_____

NEXT WEEK AT A GLANCE

MON

TUE

WED

THU

FRI

SAT

SUN

DATE

M   T   W   Th   F   Sa   Su

▷ _____

▷ _____

▷ _____

TODAY'S TOP 3

To Do

☐ _____

☐ _____

☐ _____

☐ _____

☐ _____

☐ _____

☐ _____

☐ _____

☐ _____

☐ _____

☐ _____

Income Generating Activities

APPOINTMENTS

6am	
7am	
8am	
9am	
10am	
11am	
12pm	
1pm	
2pm	
3pm	
4pm	
5pm	
6pm	
7pm	

▷ AFFIRMATIONS

▷ SALES GOALS

▷ NOTES / IDEAS

DATE

M   T   W   Th   F   Sa   Su

➤
➤
➤

To Do

☐
☐
☐
☐
☐
☐
☐
☐
☐
☐

Income Generating Activities

APPOINTMENTS

6am	
7am	
8am	
9am	
10am	
11am	
12pm	
1pm	
2pm	
3pm	
4pm	
5pm	
6pm	
7pm	

➤ AFFIRMATIONS

➤ SALES GOALS

➤ NOTES / IDEAS

DATE

M   T   W   Th   F   Sa   Su

TODAY'S TOP 3

➤ _____

➤ _____

➤ _____

To Do

☐ _____
☐ _____
☐ _____
☐ _____
☐ _____
☐ _____
☐ _____
☐ _____
☐ _____
☐ _____
☐ _____

Income Generating Activities

APPOINTMENTS

6am
7am
8am
9am
10am
11am
12pm
1pm
2pm
3pm
4pm
5pm
6pm
7pm

➤ AFFIRMATIONS

➤ SALES GOALS

➤ NOTES / IDEAS

DATE

M   T   W   Th   F   Sa   Su

▶
▶
▶

To Do

☐
☐
☐
☐
☐
☐
☐
☐
☐
☐

Income Generating Activities

APPOINTMENTS

6am
7am
8am
9am
10am
11am
12pm
1pm
2pm
3pm
4pm
5pm
6pm
7pm

▶ AFFIRMATIONS

▶ SALES GOALS

▶ NOTES / IDEAS

▷
▷
▷

TODAY'S TOP 3

To Do

- ☐
- ☐
- ☐
- ☐
- ☐
- ☐
- ☐
- ☐
- ☐
- ☐

Income Generating Activities

APPOINTMENTS

6am
7am
8am
9am
10am
11am
12pm
1pm
2pm
3pm
4pm
5pm
6pm
7pm

▷ AFFIRMATIONS

▷ SALES GOALS

▷ NOTES / IDEAS

DATE

M   T   W   Th   F   Sa   Su

▷ _____

▷ _____

▷ _____

TODAY'S TOP 3

To Do

- ☐ _____
- ☐ _____
- ☐ _____
- ☐ _____
- ☐ _____
- ☐ _____
- ☐ _____
- ☐ _____
- ☐ _____
- ☐ _____

Income Generating Activities

_____

_____

_____

_____

_____

_____

_____

_____

APPOINTMENTS

6am _____

7am _____

8am _____

9am _____

10am _____

11am _____

12pm _____

1pm _____

2pm _____

3pm _____

4pm _____

5pm _____

6pm _____

7pm _____

▷ AFFIRMATIONS

▷ SALES GOALS

▷ NOTES / IDEAS

DATE

M T W Th F Sa Su

▶ _____

▶ _____

▶ _____

TODAY'S TOP 3

To Do

☐ _____

☐ _____

☐ _____

☐ _____

☐ _____

☐ _____

☐ _____

☐ _____

☐ _____

☐ _____

☐ _____

Income Generating Activities

APPOINTMENTS

6am

7am

8am

9am

10am

11am

12pm

1pm

2pm

3pm

4pm

5pm

6pm

7pm

▶ AFFIRMATIONS

▶ SALES GOALS

▶ NOTES / IDEAS

THIS WEEK IN REVIEW

This Week's Big Wins

- ☐ _____
- ☐ _____
- ☐ _____
- ☐ _____
- ☐ _____
- ☐ _____
- ☐ _____
- ☐ _____

NOTES

_____

_____

_____

_____

_____

_____

_____

NEXT WEEK AT A GLANCE

MON _____

TUE _____

WED _____

THU _____

FRI _____

SAT _____

SUN _____

DATE

M   T   W   Th   F   Sa   Su

TODAY'S TOP 3

To Do

- [ ]
- [ ]
- [ ]
- [ ]
- [ ]
- [ ]
- [ ]
- [ ]
- [ ]
- [ ]
- [ ]

Income Generating Activities

APPOINTMENTS

6am	
7am	
8am	
9am	
10am	
11am	
12pm	
1pm	
2pm	
3pm	
4pm	
5pm	
6pm	
7pm	

AFFIRMATIONS

SALES GOALS

NOTES / IDEAS

DATE

M   T   W   Th   F   Sa   Su

▷ _____

▷ _____

▷ _____

To Do

- ☐
- ☐
- ☐
- ☐
- ☐
- ☐
- ☐
- ☐
- ☐
- ☐
- ☐

Income Generating Activities

APPOINTMENTS

6am

7am

8am

9am

10am

11am

12pm

1pm

2pm

3pm

4pm

5pm

6pm

7pm

▷ AFFIRMATIONS

▷ SALES GOALS

▷ NOTES / IDEAS

▷

▷

▷

TODAY'S TOP 3

To Do

☐

☐

☐

☐

☐

☐

☐

☐

☐

☐

☐

Income Generating Activities

APPOINTMENTS

6am	
7am	
8am	
9am	
10am	
11am	
12pm	
1pm	
2pm	
3pm	
4pm	
5pm	
6pm	
7pm	

▷ AFFIRMATIONS

▷ SALES GOALS

▷ NOTES / IDEAS

DATE

M   T   W   Th   F   Sa   Su

▶ ....

▶ ....

▶ ....

To Do

☐
☐
☐
☐
☐
☐
☐
☐
☐
☐

Income Generating Activities

APPOINTMENTS

6am
7am
8am
9am
10am
11am
12pm
1pm
2pm
3pm
4pm
5pm
6pm
7pm

▶ AFFIRMATIONS

▶ SALES GOALS

▶ NOTES / IDEAS

DATE

M   T   W   Th   F   Sa   Su

▷ ....

▷ ....

▷ ....

To Do

☐ ....

☐ ....

☐ ....

☐ ....

☐ ....

☐ ....

☐ ....

☐ ....

☐ ....

☐ ....

☐ ....

Income Generating Activities

APPOINTMENTS

6am

7am

8am

9am

10am

11am

12pm

1pm

2pm

3pm

4pm

5pm

6pm

7pm

▷ AFFIRMATIONS

▷ SALES GOALS

▷ NOTES / IDEAS

DATE

| M | T | W | Th | F | Sa | Su |

▷
▷
▷

To Do

- [ ]
- [ ]
- [ ]
- [ ]
- [ ]
- [ ]
- [ ]
- [ ]
- [ ]
- [ ]

Income Generating Activities

APPOINTMENTS

6am	
7am	
8am	
9am	
10am	
11am	
12pm	
1pm	
2pm	
3pm	
4pm	
5pm	
6pm	
7pm	

▷ AFFIRMATIONS

▷ SALES GOALS

▷ NOTES / IDEAS

DATE

M   T   W   Th   F   Sa   Su

TODAY'S TOP 3

To Do

☐
☐
☐
☐
☐
☐
☐
☐
☐
☐

Income Generating Activities

APPOINTMENTS

6am
7am
8am
9am
10am
11am
12pm
1pm
2pm
3pm
4pm
5pm
6pm
7pm

AFFIRMATIONS

SALES GOALS

NOTES / IDEAS

THIS WEEK IN REVIEW

This Week's Big Wins

- ☐ _____
- ☐ _____
- ☐ _____
- ☐ _____
- ☐ _____
- ☐ _____
- ☐ _____
- ☐ _____

NOTES

_____

_____

_____

_____

_____

_____

NEXT WEEK AT A GLANCE

MON _____

TUE _____

WED _____

THU _____

FRI _____

SAT _____

SUN _____

DATE

M   T   W   Th   F   Sa   Su

▷ _____

▷ _____

▷ _____

To Do

- ☐
- ☐
- ☐
- ☐
- ☐
- ☐
- ☐
- ☐
- ☐
- ☐
- ☐

Income Generating Activities

APPOINTMENTS

6am	
7am	▷ **AFFIRMATIONS**
8am	
9am	
10am	
11am	▷ **SALES GOALS**
12pm	
1pm	
2pm	
3pm	
4pm	▷ **NOTES / IDEAS**
5pm	
6pm	
7pm	

DATE

M   T   W   Th   F   Sa   Su

TODAY'S TOP 3

To Do

- [ ]
- [ ]
- [ ]
- [ ]
- [ ]
- [ ]
- [ ]
- [ ]
- [ ]
- [ ]

Income Generating Activities

APPOINTMENTS

6am

7am

8am

9am

10am

11am

12pm

1pm

2pm

3pm

4pm

5pm

6pm

7pm

AFFIRMATIONS

SALES GOALS

NOTES / IDEAS

DATE

M   T   W   Th   F   Sa   Su

▶ ....

▶ ....

▶ ....

TODAY'S TOP 3

To Do

- [ ]
- [ ]
- [ ]
- [ ]
- [ ]
- [ ]
- [ ]
- [ ]
- [ ]
- [ ]

Income Generating Activities

APPOINTMENTS

6am

7am

8am

9am

10am

11am

12pm

1pm

2pm

3pm

4pm

5pm

6pm

7pm

▶ AFFIRMATIONS

▶ SALES GOALS

▶ NOTES / IDEAS

DATE

M   T   W   Th   F   Sa   Su

TODAY'S TOP 3

To Do

- ☐
- ☐
- ☐
- ☐
- ☐
- ☐
- ☐
- ☐
- ☐
- ☐
- ☐

Income Generating Activities

APPOINTMENTS

6am	**AFFIRMATIONS**
7am	
8am	
9am	
10am	
11am	**SALES GOALS**
12pm	
1pm	
2pm	
3pm	
4pm	**NOTES / IDEAS**
5pm	
6pm	
7pm	

M   T   W   Th   F   Sa   Su

▷ _____

▷ _____

▷ _____

TODAY'S TOP 3

To Do

☐ _____

☐ _____

☐ _____

☐ _____

☐ _____

☐ _____

☐ _____

☐ _____

☐ _____

☐ _____

☐ _____

Income Generating Activities

_____

_____

_____

_____

_____

_____

_____

_____

_____

_____

APPOINTMENTS

6am _____

7am _____

8am _____

9am _____

10am _____

11am _____

12pm _____

1pm _____

2pm _____

3pm _____

4pm _____

5pm _____

6pm _____

7pm _____

▷ AFFIRMATIONS

▷ SALES GOALS

▷ NOTES / IDEAS

DATE

M   T   W   Th   F   Sa   Su

TODAY'S TOP 3

To Do

- [ ]
- [ ]
- [ ]
- [ ]
- [ ]
- [ ]
- [ ]
- [ ]
- [ ]
- [ ]

Income Generating Activities

APPOINTMENTS

6am	
7am	
8am	
9am	
10am	
11am	
12pm	
1pm	
2pm	
3pm	
4pm	
5pm	
6pm	
7pm	

AFFIRMATIONS

SALES GOALS

NOTES / IDEAS

DATE			M	T	W	Th	F	Sa	Su

▷ _____

▷ _____

▷ _____

TODAY'S TOP 3

To Do

- ☐ _____
- ☐ _____
- ☐ _____
- ☐ _____
- ☐ _____
- ☐ _____
- ☐ _____
- ☐ _____
- ☐ _____
- ☐ _____
- ☐ _____

Income Generating Activities

APPOINTMENTS

6am

7am

8am

9am

10am

11am

12pm

1pm

2pm

3pm

4pm

5pm

6pm

7pm

▷ AFFIRMATIONS

▷ SALES GOALS

▷ NOTES / IDEAS

THIS WEEK IN REVIEW

This Week's Big Wins

- [ ]
- [ ]
- [ ]
- [ ]
- [ ]
- [ ]
- [ ]

NOTES

NEXT WEEK AT A GLANCE

MON

TUE

WED

THU

FRI

SAT

SUN

DATE   M   T   W   Th   F   Sa   Su

▷ _____

▷ _____

▷ _____

TODAY'S TOP 3

To Do

- ☐
- ☐
- ☐
- ☐
- ☐
- ☐
- ☐
- ☐
- ☐
- ☐

Income Generating Activities

APPOINTMENTS

6am	
7am	
8am	
9am	
10am	
11am	
12pm	
1pm	
2pm	
3pm	
4pm	
5pm	
6pm	
7pm	

▷ AFFIRMATIONS

▷ SALES GOALS

▷ NOTES / IDEAS

DATE

M   T   W   Th   F   Sa   Su

TODAY'S TOP 3

To Do

- [ ]
- [ ]
- [ ]
- [ ]
- [ ]
- [ ]
- [ ]
- [ ]
- [ ]
- [ ]

Income Generating Activities

APPOINTMENTS

6am	
7am	
8am	
9am	
10am	
11am	
12pm	
1pm	
2pm	
3pm	
4pm	
5pm	
6pm	
7pm	

AFFIRMATIONS

SALES GOALS

NOTES / IDEAS

DATE

M   T   W   Th   F   Sa   Su

TODAY'S TOP 3

▷ ....

▷ ....

▷ ....

To Do

☐ ....

☐ ....

☐ ....

☐ ....

☐ ....

☐ ....

☐ ....

☐ ....

☐ ....

☐ ....

☐ ....

Income Generating Activities

APPOINTMENTS

6am
7am
8am
9am
10am
11am
12pm
1pm
2pm
3pm
4pm
5pm
6pm
7pm

▷ AFFIRMATIONS

▷ SALES GOALS

▷ NOTES / IDEAS

DATE

M   T   W   Th   F   Sa   Su

▷ _____

▷ _____

▷ _____

To Do

- ☐ _____
- ☐ _____
- ☐ _____
- ☐ _____
- ☐ _____
- ☐ _____
- ☐ _____
- ☐ _____
- ☐ _____
- ☐ _____

Income Generating Activities

APPOINTMENTS

6am	
7am	
8am	
9am	
10am	
11am	
12pm	
1pm	
2pm	
3pm	
4pm	
5pm	
6pm	
7pm	

▷ AFFIRMATIONS

▷ SALES GOALS

▷ NOTES / IDEAS

DATE

M T W Th F Sa Su

▷
▷
▷

To Do

☐
☐
☐
☐
☐
☐
☐
☐
☐
☐
☐

Income Generating Activities

APPOINTMENTS

6am
7am
8am
9am
10am
11am
12pm
1pm
2pm
3pm
4pm
5pm
6pm
7pm

▷ AFFIRMATIONS

▷ SALES GOALS

▷ NOTES / IDEAS

DATE

M T W Th F Sa Su

▷
▷
▷

TODAY'S TOP 3

To Do

☐
☐
☐
☐
☐
☐
☐
☐
☐
☐

Income Generating Activities

APPOINTMENTS

6am
7am
8am
9am
10am
11am
12pm
1pm
2pm
3pm
4pm
5pm
6pm
7pm

▷ AFFIRMATIONS

▷ SALES GOALS

▷ NOTES / IDEAS

DATE

M T W Th F Sa Su

TODAY'S TOP 3

▷ _____

▷ _____

▷ _____

To Do

- ☐ _____
- ☐ _____
- ☐ _____
- ☐ _____
- ☐ _____
- ☐ _____
- ☐ _____
- ☐ _____
- ☐ _____
- ☐ _____
- ☐ _____

Income Generating Activities

APPOINTMENTS

6am

7am

8am

9am

10am

11am

12pm

1pm

2pm

3pm

4pm

5pm

6pm

7pm

▷ AFFIRMATIONS

▷ SALES GOALS

▷ NOTES / IDEAS

THIS WEEK IN REVIEW

This Week's Big Wins

- [ ]
- [ ]
- [ ]
- [ ]
- [ ]
- [ ]
- [ ]
- [ ]

NOTES

NEXT WEEK AT A GLANCE

MON

TUE

WED

THU

FRI

SAT

SUN

MONTHLY WINS

▷
▷

▷
▷

▷
▷

▷
▷

INCOME GENERATING HABITS THAT SUPPORT MONTHLY GOALS

▷   ☐ DAILY HABIT   ☐ WEEKLY HABIT

▷   ☐ DAILY HABIT   ☐ WEEKLY HABIT

▷   ☐ DAILY HABIT   ☐ WEEKLY HABIT

▷   ☐ DAILY HABIT   ☐ WEEKLY HABIT

▷   ☐ DAILY HABIT   ☐ WEEKLY HABIT

DAILY SALES

1.	11.	21.
2.	12.	22.
3.	13.	23.
4.	14.	24.
5.	15.	25.
6.	16.	26.
7.	17.	27.
8.	18.	28.
9.	19.	29.
10.	20.	30.

▷ *Success is a journey, not a destination.*

Always Do Your Best

MONTH _____

SUNDAY	MONDAY	TUESDAY	WEDNESDAY

Enjoy the little things.

THURSDAY	FRIDAY	SATURDAY	NOTES

▷ _____

▷ _____

▷ _____

TODAY'S TOP 3

To Do

☐ _____

☐ _____

☐ _____

☐ _____

☐ _____

☐ _____

☐ _____

☐ _____

☐ _____

☐ _____

☐ _____

Income Generating Activities

APPOINTMENTS

6am

7am

8am

9am

10am

11am

12pm

1pm

2pm

3pm

4pm

5pm

6pm

7pm

▷ AFFIRMATIONS

▷ SALES GOALS

▷ NOTES / IDEAS

DATE

M   T   W   Th   F   Sa   Su

▷
▷
▷

TODAY'S TOP 3

To Do

- ☐
- ☐
- ☐
- ☐
- ☐
- ☐
- ☐
- ☐
- ☐
- ☐

Income Generating Activities

APPOINTMENTS

6am
7am
8am
9am
10am
11am
12pm
1pm
2pm
3pm
4pm
5pm
6pm
7pm

▷ AFFIRMATIONS

▷ SALES GOALS

▷ NOTES / IDEAS

DATE

M   T   W   Th   F   Sa   Su

▶ ....

▶ ....

▶ ....

TODAY'S TOP 3

To Do

- ☐
- ☐
- ☐
- ☐
- ☐
- ☐
- ☐
- ☐
- ☐
- ☐
- ☐

Income Generating Activities

APPOINTMENTS

6am

7am

8am

9am

10am

11am

12pm

1pm

2pm

3pm

4pm

5pm

6pm

7pm

▷ AFFIRMATIONS

▷ SALES GOALS

▷ NOTES / IDEAS

DATE

M   T   W   Th   F   Sa   Su

TODAY'S TOP 3

To Do

- [ ]
- [ ]
- [ ]
- [ ]
- [ ]
- [ ]
- [ ]
- [ ]
- [ ]
- [ ]

Income Generating Activities

APPOINTMENTS

6am
7am
8am
9am
10am
11am
12pm
1pm
2pm
3pm
4pm
5pm
6pm
7pm

AFFIRMATIONS

SALES GOALS

NOTES / IDEAS

DATE

M T W Th F Sa Su

▷ _____

▷ _____

▷ _____

TODAY'S TOP 3

To Do

- ☐ _____
- ☐ _____
- ☐ _____
- ☐ _____
- ☐ _____
- ☐ _____
- ☐ _____
- ☐ _____
- ☐ _____
- ☐ _____
- ☐ _____

Income Generating Activities

APPOINTMENTS

6am

7am

8am

9am

10am

11am

12pm

1pm

2pm

3pm

4pm

5pm

6pm

7pm

▷ AFFIRMATIONS

▷ SALES GOALS

▷ NOTES / IDEAS

DATE

M   T   W   Th   F   Sa   Su

▷

▷

▷

TODAY'S TOP 3

To Do

- ☐
- ☐
- ☐
- ☐
- ☐
- ☐
- ☐
- ☐
- ☐
- ☐

Income Generating Activities

APPOINTMENTS

6am

7am

8am

9am

10am

11am

12pm

1pm

2pm

3pm

4pm

5pm

6pm

7pm

▷ AFFIRMATIONS

▷ SALES GOALS

▷ NOTES / IDEAS

DATE

M   T   W   Th   F   Sa   Su

⟫ ....

⟫ ....

⟫ ....

TODAY'S TOP 3

To Do

- ☐ ....
- ☐ ....
- ☐ ....
- ☐ ....
- ☐ ....
- ☐ ....
- ☐ ....
- ☐ ....
- ☐ ....
- ☐ ....
- ☐ ....

Income Generating Activities

APPOINTMENTS

6am

7am

8am

9am

10am

11am

12pm

1pm

2pm

3pm

4pm

5pm

6pm

7pm

⟫ AFFIRMATIONS

⟫ SALES GOALS

⟫ NOTES / IDEAS

THIS WEEK IN REVIEW

This Week's Big Wins

☐ _____

☐ _____

☐ _____

☐ _____

☐ _____

☐ _____

☐ _____

☐ _____

NOTES

_____

_____

_____

_____

_____

_____

_____

NEXT WEEK AT A GLANCE

MON _____

TUE _____

WED _____

THU _____

FRI _____

SAT _____

SUN _____

DATE

M T W Th F Sa Su

TODAY'S TOP 3

To Do

- [ ]
- [ ]
- [ ]
- [ ]
- [ ]
- [ ]
- [ ]
- [ ]
- [ ]
- [ ]

Income Generating Activities

APPOINTMENTS

6am
7am
8am
9am
10am
11am
12pm
1pm
2pm
3pm
4pm
5pm
6pm
7pm

AFFIRMATIONS

SALES GOALS

NOTES / IDEAS

DATE

M T W Th F Sa Su

TODAY'S TOP 3

▷ _____
▷ _____
▷ _____

To Do

☐ _____
☐ _____
☐ _____
☐ _____
☐ _____
☐ _____
☐ _____
☐ _____
☐ _____

Income Generating Activities

APPOINTMENTS

6am
7am
8am
9am
10am
11am
12pm
1pm
2pm
3pm
4pm
5pm
6pm
7pm

▷ AFFIRMATIONS

▷ SALES GOALS

▷ NOTES / IDEAS

DATE

M T W Th F Sa Su

▷ ....

▷ ....

▷ ....

To Do

☐ ....

☐ ....

☐ ....

☐ ....

☐ ....

☐ ....

☐ ....

☐ ....

☐ ....

☐ ....

Income Generating Activities

APPOINTMENTS

6am
7am
8am
9am
10am
11am
12pm
1pm
2pm
3pm
4pm
5pm
6pm
7pm

▷ AFFIRMATIONS

▷ SALES GOALS

▷ NOTES / IDEAS

DATE

M　T　W　Th　F　Sa　Su

▷ _____

▷ _____

▷ _____

TODAY'S TOP 3

To Do

- ☐ _____
- ☐ _____
- ☐ _____
- ☐ _____
- ☐ _____
- ☐ _____
- ☐ _____
- ☐ _____
- ☐ _____
- ☐ _____
- ☐ _____

Income Generating Activities

_____

_____

_____

_____

_____

_____

_____

_____

_____

APPOINTMENTS

6am _____

7am _____

8am _____

9am _____

10am _____

11am _____

12pm _____

1pm _____

2pm _____

3pm _____

4pm _____

5pm _____

6pm _____

7pm _____

▷ AFFIRMATIONS

▷ SALES GOALS

▷ NOTES / IDEAS

DATE

M T W Th F Sa Su

▷ _____

▷ _____

▷ _____

TODAY'S TOP 3

To Do

- ☐ _____
- ☐ _____
- ☐ _____
- ☐ _____
- ☐ _____
- ☐ _____
- ☐ _____
- ☐ _____
- ☐ _____
- ☐ _____
- ☐ _____

Income Generating Activities

APPOINTMENTS

6am

7am

8am

9am

10am

11am

12pm

1pm

2pm

3pm

4pm

5pm

6pm

7pm

▷ AFFIRMATIONS

▷ SALES GOALS

▷ NOTES / IDEAS

DATE

M   T   W   Th   F   Sa   Su

▷ ....

▷ ....

▷ ....

TODAY'S TOP 3

To Do

- ☐
- ☐
- ☐
- ☐
- ☐
- ☐
- ☐
- ☐
- ☐
- ☐

Income Generating Activities

APPOINTMENTS

| 6am |
| 7am |
| 8am |
| 9am |
| 10am |
| 11am |
| 12pm |
| 1pm |
| 2pm |
| 3pm |
| 4pm |
| 5pm |
| 6pm |
| 7pm |

▷ AFFIRMATIONS

▷ SALES GOALS

▷ NOTES / IDEAS

DATE

M   T   W   Th   F   Sa   Su

➤ _____

➤ _____

➤ _____

To Do

- ☐ _____
- ☐ _____
- ☐ _____
- ☐ _____
- ☐ _____
- ☐ _____
- ☐ _____
- ☐ _____
- ☐ _____
- ☐ _____
- ☐ _____

Income Generating Activities

APPOINTMENTS

6am

7am

8am

9am

10am

11am

12pm

1pm

2pm

3pm

4pm

5pm

6pm

7pm

➤ AFFIRMATIONS

➤ SALES GOALS

➤ NOTES / IDEAS

THIS WEEK IN REVIEW
This Week's Big Wins

- ☐
- ☐
- ☐
- ☐
- ☐
- ☐
- ☐
- ☐

NOTES

NEXT WEEK AT A GLANCE

MON

TUE

WED

THU

FRI

SAT

SUN

DATE

M   T   W   Th   F   Sa   Su

‣ _____

‣ _____

‣ _____

TODAY'S TOP 3

To Do

- ☐
- ☐
- ☐
- ☐
- ☐
- ☐
- ☐
- ☐
- ☐
- ☐

Income Generating Activities

APPOINTMENTS

6am

7am

8am

9am

10am

11am

12pm

1pm

2pm

3pm

4pm

5pm

6pm

7pm

‣ AFFIRMATIONS

‣ SALES GOALS

‣ NOTES / IDEAS

DATE

M T W Th F Sa Su

▷ _____

▷ _____

▷ _____

To Do

- ☐ _____
- ☐ _____
- ☐ _____
- ☐ _____
- ☐ _____
- ☐ _____
- ☐ _____
- ☐ _____
- ☐ _____
- ☐ _____

Income Generating Activities

_____

_____

_____

_____

_____

_____

_____

_____

_____

APPOINTMENTS

6am _____

7am _____

8am _____

9am _____

10am _____

11am _____

12pm _____

1pm _____

2pm _____

3pm _____

4pm _____

5pm _____

6pm _____

7pm _____

▷ **AFFIRMATIONS**

▷ **SALES GOALS**

▷ **NOTES / IDEAS**

DATE			M	T	W	Th	F	Sa	Su

▷ _____

▷ _____

▷ _____

To Do

- ☐ _____
- ☐ _____
- ☐ _____
- ☐ _____
- ☐ _____
- ☐ _____
- ☐ _____
- ☐ _____
- ☐ _____
- ☐ _____
- ☐ _____

Income Generating Activities

_____

_____

_____

_____

_____

_____

_____

_____

_____

APPOINTMENTS

6am _____

7am _____

8am _____

9am _____

10am _____

11am _____

12pm _____

1pm _____

2pm _____

3pm _____

4pm _____

5pm _____

6pm _____

7pm _____

▷ AFFIRMATIONS

▷ SALES GOALS

▷ NOTES / IDEAS

DATE

M   T   W   Th   F   Sa   Su

▷ ....

▷ ....

▷ ....

TODAY'S TOP 3

To Do

☐
☐
☐
☐
☐
☐
☐
☐
☐
☐

Income Generating Activities

APPOINTMENTS

6am

7am

8am

9am

10am

11am

12pm

1pm

2pm

3pm

4pm

5pm

6pm

7pm

▷ AFFIRMATIONS

▷ SALES GOALS

▷ NOTES / IDEAS

DATE

M   T   W   Th   F   Sa   Su

⊳ _____

⊳ _____

⊳ _____

To Do

☐ _____

☐ _____

☐ _____

☐ _____

☐ _____

☐ _____

☐ _____

☐ _____

☐ _____

☐ _____

☐ _____

Income Generating Activities

APPOINTMENTS

6am _____

7am _____

8am _____

9am _____

10am _____

11am _____

12pm _____

1pm _____

2pm _____

3pm _____

4pm _____

5pm _____

6pm _____

7pm _____

⊳ AFFIRMATIONS

⊳ SALES GOALS

⊳ NOTES / IDEAS

DATE

M   T   W   Th   F   Sa   Su

▷ _____

▷ _____

▷ _____

To Do

- ☐ _____
- ☐ _____
- ☐ _____
- ☐ _____
- ☐ _____
- ☐ _____
- ☐ _____
- ☐ _____
- ☐ _____
- ☐ _____

Income Generating Activities

_____

_____

_____

_____

_____

_____

_____

_____

_____

_____

APPOINTMENTS

6am _____

7am _____

8am _____

9am _____

10am _____

11am _____

12pm _____

1pm _____

2pm _____

3pm _____

4pm _____

5pm _____

6pm _____

7pm _____

▷ AFFIRMATIONS

▷ SALES GOALS

▷ NOTES / IDEAS

DATE

M T W Th F Sa Su

▷ _____

▷ _____

▷ _____

To Do

☐ _____
☐ _____
☐ _____
☐ _____
☐ _____
☐ _____
☐ _____
☐ _____
☐ _____
☐ _____
☐ _____

Income Generating Activities

APPOINTMENTS

6am	
7am	▷ **AFFIRMATIONS**
8am	
9am	
10am	
11am	▷ **SALES GOALS**
12pm	
1pm	
2pm	
3pm	
4pm	▷ **NOTES / IDEAS**
5pm	
6pm	
7pm	

THIS WEEK IN REVIEW

This Week's Big Wins

- [ ] _____
- [ ] _____
- [ ] _____
- [ ] _____
- [ ] _____
- [ ] _____
- [ ] _____
- [ ] _____

NOTES

_____

_____

_____

_____

_____

_____

_____

NEXT WEEK AT A GLANCE

MON _____

TUE _____

WED _____

THU _____

FRI _____

SAT _____

SUN _____

DATE

M   T   W   Th   F   Sa   Su

▷ ....

▷ ....

▷ ....

TODAY'S TOP 3

To Do

- ☐ ....
- ☐ ....
- ☐ ....
- ☐ ....
- ☐ ....
- ☐ ....
- ☐ ....
- ☐ ....
- ☐ ....
- ☐ ....

Income Generating Activities

APPOINTMENTS

6am

7am

8am

9am

10am

11am

12pm

1pm

2pm

3pm

4pm

5pm

6pm

7pm

▷ AFFIRMATIONS

▷ SALES GOALS

▷ NOTES / IDEAS

DATE

M   T   W   Th   F   Sa   Su

▷
▷
▷

To Do

☐
☐
☐
☐
☐
☐
☐
☐
☐
☐

Income Generating Activities

APPOINTMENTS

6am
7am
8am
9am
10am
11am
12pm
1pm
2pm
3pm
4pm
5pm
6pm
7pm

▷ AFFIRMATIONS

▷ SALES GOALS

▷ NOTES / IDEAS

DATE

M T W Th F Sa Su

▷
▷
▷

To Do

☐
☐
☐
☐
☐
☐
☐
☐
☐
☐
☐

Income Generating Activities

APPOINTMENTS

6am
7am
8am
9am
10am
11am
12pm
1pm
2pm
3pm
4pm
5pm
6pm
7pm

▷ AFFIRMATIONS

▷ SALES GOALS

▷ NOTES / IDEAS

DATE

M   T   W   Th   F   Sa   Su

▷ _____

▷ _____

▷ _____

TODAY'S TOP 3

To Do

☐ _____
☐ _____
☐ _____
☐ _____
☐ _____
☐ _____
☐ _____
☐ _____
☐ _____
☐ _____

Income Generating Activities

APPOINTMENTS

6am
7am
8am
9am
10am
11am
12pm
1pm
2pm
3pm
4pm
5pm
6pm
7pm

▷ AFFIRMATIONS

▷ SALES GOALS

▷ NOTES / IDEAS

DATE

M   T   W   Th   F   Sa   Su

TODAY'S TOP 3

To Do

- [ ]
- [ ]
- [ ]
- [ ]
- [ ]
- [ ]
- [ ]
- [ ]
- [ ]
- [ ]
- [ ]

Income Generating Activities

APPOINTMENTS

6am	
7am	
8am	
9am	
10am	
11am	
12pm	
1pm	
2pm	
3pm	
4pm	
5pm	
6pm	
7pm	

AFFIRMATIONS

SALES GOALS

NOTES / IDEAS

DATE

M   T   W   Th   F   Sa   Su

▷ _____

▷ _____

▷ _____

TODAY'S TOP 3

To Do

- ☐
- ☐
- ☐
- ☐
- ☐
- ☐
- ☐
- ☐
- ☐
- ☐

Income Generating Activities

APPOINTMENTS

6am
7am
8am
9am
10am
11am
12pm
1pm
2pm
3pm
4pm
5pm
6pm
7pm

▷ AFFIRMATIONS

▷ SALES GOALS

▷ NOTES / IDEAS

To Do

- [ ]
- [ ]
- [ ]
- [ ]
- [ ]
- [ ]
- [ ]
- [ ]
- [ ]
- [ ]
- [ ]

Income Generating Activities

APPOINTMENTS

6am

7am

8am

9am

10am

11am

12pm

1pm

2pm

3pm

4pm

5pm

6pm

7pm

AFFIRMATIONS

SALES GOALS

NOTES / IDEAS

THIS WEEK IN REVIEW

This Week's Big Wins

☐ _____

☐ _____

☐ _____

☐ _____

☐ _____

☐ _____

☐ _____

☐ _____

NOTES

_____

_____

_____

_____

_____

_____

_____

NEXT WEEK AT A GLANCE

MON _____

TUE _____

WED _____

THU _____

FRI _____

SAT _____

SUN _____

DATE

M   T   W   Th   F   Sa   Su

▷

▷

▷

TODAY'S TOP 3

To Do

- ☐
- ☐
- ☐
- ☐
- ☐
- ☐
- ☐
- ☐
- ☐
- ☐

Income Generating Activities

APPOINTMENTS

6am

7am

8am

9am

10am

11am

12pm

1pm

2pm

3pm

4pm

5pm

6pm

7pm

▷ AFFIRMATIONS

▷ SALES GOALS

▷ NOTES / IDEAS

DATE

M   T   W   Th   F   Sa   Su

TODAY'S TOP 3

To Do

- [ ]
- [ ]
- [ ]
- [ ]
- [ ]
- [ ]
- [ ]
- [ ]
- [ ]
- [ ]

Income Generating Activities

APPOINTMENTS

6am

7am

8am

9am

10am

11am

12pm

1pm

2pm

3pm

4pm

5pm

6pm

7pm

AFFIRMATIONS

SALES GOALS

NOTES / IDEAS

DATE

M   T   W   Th   F   Sa   Su

▷

▷

▷

TODAY'S TOP 3

To Do

- ☐
- ☐
- ☐
- ☐
- ☐
- ☐
- ☐
- ☐
- ☐
- ☐
- ☐

Income Generating Activities

APPOINTMENTS

6am	
7am	▷ **AFFIRMATIONS**
8am	
9am	
10am	
11am	▷ **SALES GOALS**
12pm	
1pm	
2pm	
3pm	
4pm	▷ **NOTES / IDEAS**
5pm	
6pm	
7pm	

DATE

M   T   W   Th   F   Sa   Su

TODAY'S TOP 3

To Do

- [ ]
- [ ]
- [ ]
- [ ]
- [ ]
- [ ]
- [ ]
- [ ]
- [ ]
- [ ]

Income Generating Activities

APPOINTMENTS

6am
7am
8am
9am
10am
11am
12pm
1pm
2pm
3pm
4pm
5pm
6pm
7pm

AFFIRMATIONS

SALES GOALS

NOTES / IDEAS

DATE

M　T　W　Th　F　Sa　Su

- ▷ _____
- ▷ _____
- ▷ _____

To Do

- ☐ _____
- ☐ _____
- ☐ _____
- ☐ _____
- ☐ _____
- ☐ _____
- ☐ _____
- ☐ _____
- ☐ _____
- ☐ _____
- ☐ _____

Income Generating Activities

APPOINTMENTS

6am	
7am	
8am	
9am	
10am	
11am	
12pm	
1pm	
2pm	
3pm	
4pm	
5pm	
6pm	
7pm	

▷ AFFIRMATIONS

▷ SALES GOALS

▷ NOTES / IDEAS

DATE

M   T   W   Th   F   Sa   Su

▷
▷
▷

To Do

☐
☐
☐
☐
☐
☐
☐
☐
☐
☐

Income Generating Activities

APPOINTMENTS

6am
7am
8am
9am
10am
11am
12pm
1pm
2pm
3pm
4pm
5pm
6pm
7pm

▷ AFFIRMATIONS

▷ SALES GOALS

▷ NOTES / IDEAS

DATE

M   T   W   Th   F   Sa   Su

▷

▷

▷

TODAY'S TOP 3

To Do

- ☐
- ☐
- ☐
- ☐
- ☐
- ☐
- ☐
- ☐
- ☐
- ☐
- ☐

Income Generating Activities

APPOINTMENTS

6am

7am

8am

9am

10am

11am

12pm

1pm

2pm

3pm

4pm

5pm

6pm

7pm

▷ AFFIRMATIONS

▷ SALES GOALS

▷ NOTES / IDEAS

THIS WEEK IN REVIEW

This Week's Big Wins

- [ ]
- [ ]
- [ ]
- [ ]
- [ ]
- [ ]
- [ ]
- [ ]

NOTES

NEXT WEEK AT A GLANCE

MON

TUE

WED

THU

FRI

SAT

SUN

_____ MONTH IN REVIEW

MONTHLY WINS

▷
▷
▷
▷

▷
▷
▷
▷

INCOME GENERATING HABITS THAT SUPPORT MONTHLY GOALS

▷   ☐ DAILY HABIT   ☐ WEEKLY HABIT

▷   ☐ DAILY HABIT   ☐ WEEKLY HABIT

▷   ☐ DAILY HABIT   ☐ WEEKLY HABIT

▷   ☐ DAILY HABIT   ☐ WEEKLY HABIT

▷   ☐ DAILY HABIT   ☐ WEEKLY HABIT

DAILY SALES

1.	11.	21.
2.	12.	22.
3.	13.	23.
4.	14.	24.
5.	15.	25.
6.	16.	26.
7.	17.	27.
8.	18.	28.
9.	19.	29.
10.	20.	30.

▷ *Live the life you want.*

Nothing
is
Impossible

MONTH _____

SUNDAY	MONDAY	TUESDAY	WEDNESDAY

Follow your dreams.

THURSDAY	FRIDAY	SATURDAY	NOTES

DATE

M   T   W   Th   F   Sa   Su

▷ _____

▷ _____

▷ _____

TODAY'S TOP 3

To Do

- ☐ _____
- ☐ _____
- ☐ _____
- ☐ _____
- ☐ _____
- ☐ _____
- ☐ _____
- ☐ _____
- ☐ _____
- ☐ _____

Income Generating Activities

APPOINTMENTS

6am

7am

8am

9am

10am

11am

12pm

1pm

2pm

3pm

4pm

5pm

6pm

7pm

▷ AFFIRMATIONS

▷ SALES GOALS

▷ NOTES / IDEAS

DATE

M	T	W	Th	F	Sa	Su

▷ _____

▷ _____

▷ _____

TODAY'S TOP 3

To Do

☐ _____

☐ _____

☐ _____

☐ _____

☐ _____

☐ _____

☐ _____

☐ _____

☐ _____

☐ _____

Income Generating Activities

APPOINTMENTS

6am

7am

8am

9am

10am

11am

12pm

1pm

2pm

3pm

4pm

5pm

6pm

7pm

▷ AFFIRMATIONS

▷ SALES GOALS

▷ NOTES / IDEAS

DATE

M   T   W   Th   F   Sa   Su

TODAY'S TOP 3

To Do

- [ ]
- [ ]
- [ ]
- [ ]
- [ ]
- [ ]
- [ ]
- [ ]
- [ ]
- [ ]
- [ ]

Income Generating Activities

APPOINTMENTS

6am

7am

8am

9am

10am

11am

12pm

1pm

2pm

3pm

4pm

5pm

6pm

7pm

AFFIRMATIONS

SALES GOALS

NOTES / IDEAS

DATE

M   T   W   Th   F   Sa   Su

▷ _____

▷ _____

▷ _____

TODAY'S TOP 3

To Do

- ☐ _____
- ☐ _____
- ☐ _____
- ☐ _____
- ☐ _____
- ☐ _____
- ☐ _____
- ☐ _____
- ☐ _____
- ☐ _____

Income Generating Activities

_____

_____

_____

_____

_____

_____

_____

_____

_____

APPOINTMENTS

6am _____

7am _____

8am _____

9am _____

10am _____

11am _____

12pm _____

1pm _____

2pm _____

3pm _____

4pm _____

5pm _____

6pm _____

7pm _____

▷ AFFIRMATIONS

▷ SALES GOALS

▷ NOTES / IDEAS

DATE

M T W Th F Sa Su

▷
▷
▷

To Do

- ☐
- ☐
- ☐
- ☐
- ☐
- ☐
- ☐
- ☐
- ☐
- ☐
- ☐

Income Generating Activities

APPOINTMENTS

6am
7am
8am
9am
10am
11am
12pm
1pm
2pm
3pm
4pm
5pm
6pm
7pm

▷ AFFIRMATIONS

▷ SALES GOALS

▷ NOTES / IDEAS

DATE

M   T   W   Th   F   Sa   Su

TODAY'S TOP 3

To Do

- ☐
- ☐
- ☐
- ☐
- ☐
- ☐
- ☐
- ☐
- ☐
- ☐

Income Generating Activities

APPOINTMENTS

6am
7am
8am
9am
10am
11am
12pm
1pm
2pm
3pm
4pm
5pm
6pm
7pm

AFFIRMATIONS

SALES GOALS

NOTES / IDEAS

DATE

M   T   W   Th   F   Sa   Su

TODAY'S TOP 3

To Do

- ☐
- ☐
- ☐
- ☐
- ☐
- ☐
- ☐
- ☐
- ☐
- ☐
- ☐

Income Generating Activities

APPOINTMENTS

6am

7am

8am

9am

10am

11am

12pm

1pm

2pm

3pm

4pm

5pm

6pm

7pm

AFFIRMATIONS

SALES GOALS

NOTES / IDEAS

THIS WEEK IN REVIEW

This Week's Big Wins

- ☐ _____
- ☐ _____
- ☐ _____
- ☐ _____
- ☐ _____
- ☐ _____
- ☐ _____

NOTES

_____

_____

_____

_____

_____

_____

_____

_____

MON

NEXT WEEK AT A GLANCE

TUE

WED

THU

FRI

SAT

SUN

DATE

M   T   W   Th   F   Sa   Su

▷ _____

▷ _____

▷ _____

TODAY'S TOP 3

To Do

☐ _____
☐ _____
☐ _____
☐ _____
☐ _____
☐ _____
☐ _____
☐ _____
☐ _____
☐ _____
☐ _____

Income Generating Activities

APPOINTMENTS

6am _____
7am _____
8am _____
9am _____
10am _____
11am _____
12pm _____
1pm _____
2pm _____
3pm _____
4pm _____
5pm _____
6pm _____
7pm _____

▷ AFFIRMATIONS

▷ SALES GOALS

▷ NOTES / IDEAS

DATE

M   T   W   Th   F   Sa   Su

TODAY'S TOP 3

To Do

- ☐
- ☐
- ☐
- ☐
- ☐
- ☐
- ☐
- ☐
- ☐
- ☐
- ☐

Income Generating Activities

APPOINTMENTS

6am
7am
8am
9am
10am
11am
12pm
1pm
2pm
3pm
4pm
5pm
6pm
7pm

AFFIRMATIONS

SALES GOALS

NOTES / IDEAS

DATE

M   T   W   Th   F   Sa   Su

▷ _____

▷ _____

▷ _____

TODAY'S TOP 3

To Do

☐ _____

☐ _____

☐ _____

☐ _____

☐ _____

☐ _____

☐ _____

☐ _____

☐ _____

☐ _____

☐ _____

Income Generating Activities

APPOINTMENTS

6am

7am

8am

9am

10am

11am

12pm

1pm

2pm

3pm

4pm

5pm

6pm

7pm

▷ AFFIRMATIONS

▷ SALES GOALS

▷ NOTES / IDEAS

DATE   M T W Th F Sa Su

▷

▷

▷

TODAY'S TOP 3

To Do

☐
☐
☐
☐
☐
☐
☐
☐
☐
☐

Income Generating Activities

APPOINTMENTS

6am
7am
8am
9am
10am
11am
12pm
1pm
2pm
3pm
4pm
5pm
6pm
7pm

▷ AFFIRMATIONS

▷ SALES GOALS

▷ NOTES / IDEAS

DATE   M   T   W   Th   F   Sa   Su

To Do	Income Generating Activities
☐	
☐	
☐	
☐	
☐	
☐	
☐	
☐	
☐	
☐	

APPOINTMENTS

6am	**AFFIRMATIONS**
7am	
8am	
9am	
10am	
11am	**SALES GOALS**
12pm	
1pm	
2pm	
3pm	
4pm	**NOTES / IDEAS**
5pm	
6pm	
7pm	

DATE

M   T   W   Th   F   Sa   Su

▶ _____

▶ _____

▶ _____

TODAY'S TOP 3

To Do

☐ _____

☐ _____

☐ _____

☐ _____

☐ _____

☐ _____

☐ _____

☐ _____

☐ _____

☐ _____

Income Generating Activities

APPOINTMENTS

6am

7am

8am

9am

10am

11am

12pm

1pm

2pm

3pm

4pm

5pm

6pm

7pm

▶ AFFIRMATIONS

▶ SALES GOALS

▶ NOTES / IDEAS

DATE

M   T   W   Th   F   Sa   Su

TODAY'S TOP 3

To Do

- [ ]
- [ ]
- [ ]
- [ ]
- [ ]
- [ ]
- [ ]
- [ ]
- [ ]
- [ ]
- [ ]

Income Generating Activities

APPOINTMENTS

6am
7am
8am
9am
10am
11am
12pm
1pm
2pm
3pm
4pm
5pm
6pm
7pm

AFFIRMATIONS

SALES GOALS

NOTES / IDEAS

THIS WEEK IN REVIEW

This Week's Big Wins

- [ ]
- [ ]
- [ ]
- [ ]
- [ ]
- [ ]
- [ ]
- [ ]

NOTES

MON

TUE

WED

THU

FRI

SAT

SUN

DATE		M	T	W	Th	F	Sa	Su

▷ ....

▷ ....

▷ ....

To Do

☐ ....
☐ ....
☐ ....
☐ ....
☐ ....
☐ ....
☐ ....
☐ ....
☐ ....
☐ ....
☐ ....

Income Generating Activities

APPOINTMENTS

6am
7am
8am
9am
10am
11am
12pm
1pm
2pm
3pm
4pm
5pm
6pm
7pm

▷ AFFIRMATIONS

▷ SALES GOALS

▷ NOTES / IDEAS

DATE

M　T　W　Th　F　Sa　Su

TODAY'S TOP 3

To Do

- [ ]
- [ ]
- [ ]
- [ ]
- [ ]
- [ ]
- [ ]
- [ ]
- [ ]
- [ ]

Income Generating Activities

APPOINTMENTS

6am
7am
8am
9am
10am
11am
12pm
1pm
2pm
3pm
4pm
5pm
6pm
7pm

AFFIRMATIONS

SALES GOALS

NOTES / IDEAS

DATE

M T W Th F Sa Su

TODAY'S TOP 3

▷ _____

▷ _____

▷ _____

To Do

- ☐ _____
- ☐ _____
- ☐ _____
- ☐ _____
- ☐ _____
- ☐ _____
- ☐ _____
- ☐ _____
- ☐ _____
- ☐ _____

Income Generating Activities

APPOINTMENTS

6am _____

7am _____

8am _____

9am _____

10am _____

11am _____

12pm _____

1pm _____

2pm _____

3pm _____

4pm _____

5pm _____

6pm _____

7pm _____

▷ AFFIRMATIONS

▷ SALES GOALS

▷ NOTES / IDEAS

DATE

M   T   W   Th   F   Sa   Su

TODAY'S TOP 3

To Do

- [ ]
- [ ]
- [ ]
- [ ]
- [ ]
- [ ]
- [ ]
- [ ]
- [ ]
- [ ]

Income Generating Activities

APPOINTMENTS

6am

7am

8am

9am

10am

11am

12pm

1pm

2pm

3pm

4pm

5pm

6pm

7pm

AFFIRMATIONS

SALES GOALS

NOTES / IDEAS

DATE

M   T   W   Th   F   Sa   Su

TODAY'S TOP 3

To Do

- [ ]
- [ ]
- [ ]
- [ ]
- [ ]
- [ ]
- [ ]
- [ ]
- [ ]
- [ ]
- [ ]

Income Generating Activities

APPOINTMENTS

6am

7am

8am

9am

10am

11am

12pm

1pm

2pm

3pm

4pm

5pm

6pm

7pm

AFFIRMATIONS

SALES GOALS

NOTES / IDEAS

DATE

M   T   W   Th   F   Sa   Su

▷ _____

▷ _____

▷ _____

TODAY'S TOP 3

To Do

- ☐ _____
- ☐ _____
- ☐ _____
- ☐ _____
- ☐ _____
- ☐ _____
- ☐ _____
- ☐ _____
- ☐ _____
- ☐ _____
- ☐ _____

Income Generating Activities

APPOINTMENTS

6am _____

7am _____

8am _____

9am _____

10am _____

11am _____

12pm _____

1pm _____

2pm _____

3pm _____

4pm _____

5pm _____

6pm _____

7pm _____

▷ AFFIRMATIONS

▷ SALES GOALS

▷ NOTES / IDEAS

DATE

M T W Th F Sa Su

▷ _____

▷ _____

▷ _____

TODAY'S TOP 3

To Do

- ☐ _____
- ☐ _____
- ☐ _____
- ☐ _____
- ☐ _____
- ☐ _____
- ☐ _____
- ☐ _____
- ☐ _____
- ☐ _____
- ☐ _____

Income Generating Activities

APPOINTMENTS

6am	
7am	
8am	
9am	
10am	
11am	
12pm	
1pm	
2pm	
3pm	
4pm	
5pm	
6pm	
7pm	

▷ AFFIRMATIONS

▷ SALES GOALS

▷ NOTES / IDEAS

THIS WEEK IN REVIEW

This Week's Big Wins

- [ ]
- [ ]
- [ ]
- [ ]
- [ ]
- [ ]
- [ ]
- [ ]

NOTES

NEXT WEEK AT A GLANCE

MON

TUE

WED

THU

FRI

SAT

SUN

DATE

M T W Th F Sa Su

To Do

- [ ]
- [ ]
- [ ]
- [ ]
- [ ]
- [ ]
- [ ]
- [ ]
- [ ]
- [ ]

Income Generating Activities

APPOINTMENTS

6am

7am

8am

9am

10am

11am

12pm

1pm

2pm

3pm

4pm

5pm

6pm

7pm

AFFIRMATIONS

SALES GOALS

NOTES / IDEAS

DATE   M   T   W   Th   F   Sa   Su

TODAY'S TOP 3

To Do

- [ ]
- [ ]
- [ ]
- [ ]
- [ ]
- [ ]
- [ ]
- [ ]
- [ ]
- [ ]

Income Generating Activities

APPOINTMENTS

6am
7am
8am
9am
10am
11am
12pm
1pm
2pm
3pm
4pm
5pm
6pm
7pm

AFFIRMATIONS

SALES GOALS

NOTES / IDEAS

DATE

M   T   W   Th   F   Sa   Su

▶ _____

▶ _____

▶ _____

TODAY'S TOP 3

To Do

- ☐ _____
- ☐ _____
- ☐ _____
- ☐ _____
- ☐ _____
- ☐ _____
- ☐ _____
- ☐ _____
- ☐ _____
- ☐ _____
- ☐ _____

Income Generating Activities

APPOINTMENTS

6am	
7am	
8am	
9am	
10am	
11am	
12pm	
1pm	
2pm	
3pm	
4pm	
5pm	
6pm	
7pm	

▶ AFFIRMATIONS

▶ SALES GOALS

▶ NOTES / IDEAS

DATE

M T W Th F Sa Su

TODAY'S TOP 3

▷ _____

▷ _____

▷ _____

To Do

- ☐ _____
- ☐ _____
- ☐ _____
- ☐ _____
- ☐ _____
- ☐ _____
- ☐ _____
- ☐ _____
- ☐ _____
- ☐ _____

Income Generating Activities

APPOINTMENTS

6am

7am

8am

9am

10am

11am

12pm

1pm

2pm

3pm

4pm

5pm

6pm

7pm

▷ AFFIRMATIONS

▷ SALES GOALS

▷ NOTES / IDEAS

DATE

M T W Th F Sa Su

TODAY'S TOP 3

▷ ....

▷ ....

▷ ....

To Do

- ☐
- ☐
- ☐
- ☐
- ☐
- ☐
- ☐
- ☐
- ☐
- ☐
- ☐

Income Generating Activities

APPOINTMENTS

6am

7am

8am

9am

10am

11am

12pm

1pm

2pm

3pm

4pm

5pm

6pm

7pm

▷ AFFIRMATIONS

▷ SALES GOALS

▷ NOTES / IDEAS

DATE

M T W Th F Sa Su

TODAY'S TOP 3

▷ _____
▷ _____
▷ _____

To Do

☐ _____
☐ _____
☐ _____
☐ _____
☐ _____
☐ _____
☐ _____
☐ _____
☐ _____
☐ _____

Income Generating Activities

APPOINTMENTS

6am
7am
8am
9am
10am
11am
12pm
1pm
2pm
3pm
4pm
5pm
6pm
7pm

▷ AFFIRMATIONS

▷ SALES GOALS

▷ NOTES / IDEAS

DATE

M   T   W   Th   F   Sa   Su

▷ _____

▷ _____

▷ _____

TODAY'S TOP 3

To Do

- ☐
- ☐
- ☐
- ☐
- ☐
- ☐
- ☐
- ☐
- ☐
- ☐
- ☐

Income Generating Activities

APPOINTMENTS

6am	
7am	
8am	
9am	
10am	
11am	
12pm	
1pm	
2pm	
3pm	
4pm	
5pm	
6pm	
7pm	

▷ AFFIRMATIONS

▷ SALES GOALS

▷ NOTES / IDEAS

THIS WEEK IN REVIEW

This Week's Big Wins

- [ ]
- [ ]
- [ ]
- [ ]
- [ ]
- [ ]
- [ ]
- [ ]

NOTES

NEXT WEEK AT A GLANCE

MON

TUE

WED

THU

FRI

SAT

SUN

DATE

M T W Th F Sa Su

▷ _____

▷ _____

▷ _____

To Do

☐ _____

☐ _____

☐ _____

☐ _____

☐ _____

☐ _____

☐ _____

☐ _____

☐ _____

☐ _____

Income Generating Activities

APPOINTMENTS

6am _____

7am _____

8am _____

9am _____

10am _____

11am _____

12pm _____

1pm _____

2pm _____

3pm _____

4pm _____

5pm _____

6pm _____

7pm _____

▷ AFFIRMATIONS

▷ SALES GOALS

▷ NOTES / IDEAS

DATE

M   T   W   Th   F   Sa   Su

▷

▷

▷

TODAY'S TOP 3

To Do

- ☐
- ☐
- ☐
- ☐
- ☐
- ☐
- ☐
- ☐
- ☐
- ☐

Income Generating Activities

APPOINTMENTS

6am

7am

8am

9am

10am

11am

12pm

1pm

2pm

3pm

4pm

5pm

6pm

7pm

▷ AFFIRMATIONS

▷ SALES GOALS

▷ NOTES / IDEAS

DATE

M T W Th F Sa Su

TODAY'S TOP 3

▷ _____

▷ _____

▷ _____

To Do

☐ _____
☐ _____
☐ _____
☐ _____
☐ _____
☐ _____
☐ _____
☐ _____
☐ _____
☐ _____

Income Generating Activities

APPOINTMENTS

6am
7am
8am
9am
10am
11am
12pm
1pm
2pm
3pm
4pm
5pm
6pm
7pm

▷ AFFIRMATIONS

▷ SALES GOALS

▷ NOTES / IDEAS

DATE

M   T   W   Th   F   Sa   Su

➤
➤
➤

TODAY'S TOP 3

To Do

- [ ]
- [ ]
- [ ]
- [ ]
- [ ]
- [ ]
- [ ]
- [ ]
- [ ]
- [ ]

Income Generating Activities

APPOINTMENTS

6am
7am
8am
9am
10am
11am
12pm
1pm
2pm
3pm
4pm
5pm
6pm
7pm

➤ AFFIRMATIONS

➤ SALES GOALS

➤ NOTES / IDEAS

DATE

M T W Th F Sa Su

TODAY'S TOP 3

To Do

- [ ]
- [ ]
- [ ]
- [ ]
- [ ]
- [ ]
- [ ]
- [ ]
- [ ]
- [ ]

Income Generating Activities

APPOINTMENTS

6am
7am
8am
9am
10am
11am
12pm
1pm
2pm
3pm
4pm
5pm
6pm
7pm

AFFIRMATIONS

SALES GOALS

NOTES / IDEAS

DATE

M   T   W   Th   F   Sa   Su

▷

▷

▷

TODAY'S TOP 3

To Do

☐

☐

☐

☐

☐

☐

☐

☐

☐

☐

Income Generating Activities

APPOINTMENTS

6am

7am

8am

9am

10am

11am

12pm

1pm

2pm

3pm

4pm

5pm

6pm

7pm

▷ AFFIRMATIONS

▷ SALES GOALS

▷ NOTES / IDEAS

DATE

M   T   W   Th   F   Sa   Su

▷ _____

▷ _____

▷ _____

TODAY'S TOP 3

To Do

- ☐ _____
- ☐ _____
- ☐ _____
- ☐ _____
- ☐ _____
- ☐ _____
- ☐ _____
- ☐ _____
- ☐ _____
- ☐ _____
- ☐ _____

Income Generating Activities

APPOINTMENTS

6am

7am

8am

9am

10am

11am

12pm

1pm

2pm

3pm

4pm

5pm

6pm

7pm

▷ AFFIRMATIONS

▷ SALES GOALS

▷ NOTES / IDEAS

THIS WEEK IN REVIEW

This Week's Big Wins

- [ ]
- [ ]
- [ ]
- [ ]
- [ ]
- [ ]
- [ ]
- [ ]

NOTES

MON

NEXT WEEK AT A GLANCE

TUE

WED

THU

FRI

SAT

SUN

_____ MONTH IN REVIEW

MONTHLY WINS

▷
▷
▷
▷

▷
▷
▷
▷

INCOME GENERATING HABITS THAT SUPPORT MONTHLY GOALS

▷ _____ ☐ DAILY HABIT   ☐ WEEKLY HABIT

▷ _____ ☐ DAILY HABIT   ☐ WEEKLY HABIT

▷ _____ ☐ DAILY HABIT   ☐ WEEKLY HABIT

▷ _____ ☐ DAILY HABIT   ☐ WEEKLY HABIT

▷ _____ ☐ DAILY HABIT   ☐ WEEKLY HABIT

DAILY SALES

1.	11.	21.
2.	12.	22.
3.	13.	23.
4.	14.	24.
5.	15.	25.
6.	16.	26.
7.	17.	27.
8.	18.	28.
9.	19.	29.
10.	20.	30.

▷ *Never Give Up.*

Step back...
Start
Again

Made in the USA
Las Vegas, NV
20 December 2021